FIGHTING
HELICOPTERS
of the **20**TH
CENTURY

FIGHTING HELICOPTERS
of the 20TH CENTURY

Christopher Chant

Illustrated by John Batchelor

TIGER BOOKS INTERNATIONAL
LONDON

This edition published in 1996 by
Tiger Books International PLC, Twickenham
© Graham Beehag Books, Christchurch, Dorset
All rights reserved
Printed and bound in Singapore

ISBN 1-85501-808-X

Contents

The Early Helicopter

THE earliest type of flying machine of which there is still definite evidence was a model helicopter. It resembled a small horizontal four-bladed windmill that lifted into the air when its spindle was rotated by a drawstring. The image of this model dates from about 1325, so it seems likely that the concept of what we now call the helicopter has fascinated aviation pioneers since the early fourteenth century.

In about 1500 the great Italian polymath, artist and inventor, Leonardo da Vinci, turned his fertile mind to the helicopter, although he had no concept of true aerodynamic lift. His drawing for a helicopter demonstrates its designer's natural genius and could possibly have risen into the air if built in model form, but the design was very eccentric – it was basically an airscrew in the literal sense of the word: a helical wing which, if rotated, would have 'screwed' itself up into the air.

This and later designs might have worked in model form but would have been completely impractical in full-size form because they ignored the problems of control, most especially over the effects of the rotor's torque. Like the aeroplane, the helicopter in its definitive form is based on the concept of aerodynamic lift. While a conventional aeroplane is propelled forward so that the circulation of air past the wings generates lift, the helicopter relies on the rotation of the rotor to create the flow of air past the rotor blades for the generation of lift.

The concept of helicopter flight, incorporating as its major elements the possibility of vertical take-off and of hovering, continued to fascinate men in the centuries after Leonardo's death. Extraordinary and sometimes technically interesting models were developed, but all these pioneers lacked two essentials: a true understanding of the nature of lift and an engine of adequate power-to-weight ratio. Sir George Cayley drew up plans for a helicopter in 1796 and 1853, and in 1842 W.H. Phillips produced a fascinating model driven by a steam engine: the most interesting feature of the Phillips model were the steam jets issuing from the tips of the rotor blades to drive the lifting elements, in a torqueless fashion that still attracts the designers of helicopters.

Only with the invention of the light petrol engine towards the end of the nineteenth century, however, was it possible for the pioneers to move forward from models towards full-sized machines. Here they came face to face with the first basic problem of helicopter development, how to control the reaction to the torque of the spinning rotor: in practical terms, this means that as the blades of the rotor turn around their vertical shaft, the fuselage

Arguably the first successful helicopter, the Focke-Achgelis Fa 61 (originally the Focke-Wulf Fw 61) of 1937 was a workable although clumsy machine with two counter-rotating rotors, each possessing a diameter of 22ft 11.625in (7.00m), carried at the tips of two long outrigger arms. The helicopter was powered by a Siemens-Halske Sh.14A radial piston engine rated at 160hp (119kW), had a maximum take-off weight of 2,100lb (953kg), and was characterised by performance that included a cruising speed of 62mph (100km/h) at sea level, service ceiling of 8,600ft (2,620m) and range of 143 miles (230km).

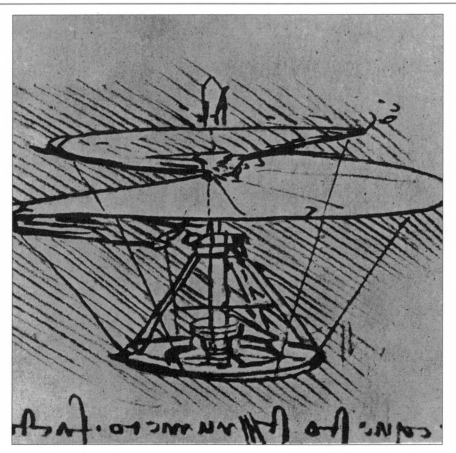

A remarkable achievement for its time (the end of the fifteenth and beginning of the sixteenth centuries, the 'helicopter' designed by Leonardo da Vinci was really a type of helical airscrew but lacked adequate motive power and also any means of control.

tends, by reaction, to rotate in the opposite direction. The pioneers saw several ways of overcoming this problem, such as the use of contra-rotating rotors on co-axial shafts, counter-rotating rotors on different shafts, or a small propeller mounted vertically at the rear end of the fuselage to hold the tail steady against the torque reaction. They could even suggest a practical means of moving the helicopter forward, backward and sideways: the axis of the rotor would be tilted to provide lift in the direction the pilot wished to take.

The problem that caused most difficulty in the development of fully practical helicopters, however, was cyclic pitch control of the type first expounded by

The Breguet-Richet Gyroplane II of 1908 was powered by a 55hp (41kW) Renault engine and was basically of aeroplane configuration with a fuselage and tail unit as well as small wings that provided an additional 538sq ft (50sq m) of lifting area to supplement the two forward-tilting rotors, each with a diameter of 25ft 9in (7.85m) for a total rotary lifting area of 1,041.9sq ft (96.8sq m). The machine made a number of successful flights in the summer of 1908 before being damaged in a heavy landing, and was then rebuilt as the Gyroplane II bis that made only one test flight before a storm wrecked the machine in its hangar during May 1909.

The Breguet-Richet Gyroplane II bis is pictured during its brief life in 1909. The loss of this machine helped to persuade Louis Breguet, also discouraged by the current lack of piston engines offering a high power-to-weight ratio, to cease work on rotary-wing aircraft until the 1930s, when he returned to the fray with the Breguet-Dorand Gyroplane Laboratoire that was probably completed in November 1933.

G.A. Crocco in 1906: when a helicopter lifts vertically in still air, the speed of the airflow over all the rotor's blades is equal and so too is the lift generated by each blade right through a complete rotation; but when the helicopter moves forward, the movement of air over any advancing blade is greater than that over any retreating blade, resulting in greater lift on the side of the advancing blades and thus a tendency to roll in the direction of the retreating blades. The solution was as readily appreciated as the problem, but the means of turning this solution into a practical method of cyclic pitch control (the adjustment of rotor blade pitch so that the lift is equal on each side of the central shaft) was altogether more taxing.

This concept of altering the rotor blades' angle of incidence as they turned, with the objective of balancing the lift by decreasing the angle of incidence of the advancing blades and increasing that of the retreating blades, was fraught with technical problems and few engineers seemed to realise exactly what was needed. The isolated figure of the Danish pioneer J.C.Ellehammer, who made interesting advances in the design of fixed-wing aircraft, was perhaps the first man to build a helicopter with adequate provision for incidence control, in 1912. The machine was unsuccessful, however, and like his fixed-wing designs it failed to become well known because of Ellehammer's solitary way of life. This was a hindrance to the evolution of flight, for Ellehammer conceived a number of technical advances that had to await reinvention by later designers.

By 1912, two French helicopters had left the ground, although neither could be said to have flown in the proper sense of the word since neither had cyclic pitch control nor any other means of adopting a given course in the air. The first was built by the Breguet brothers. Powered by a 50hp (37.3kW) Antoinette engine, this Breguet-Richet Gyroplane I first rose into the air at Douai in September 1907: four men, one at each corner of the machine, had to steady

9

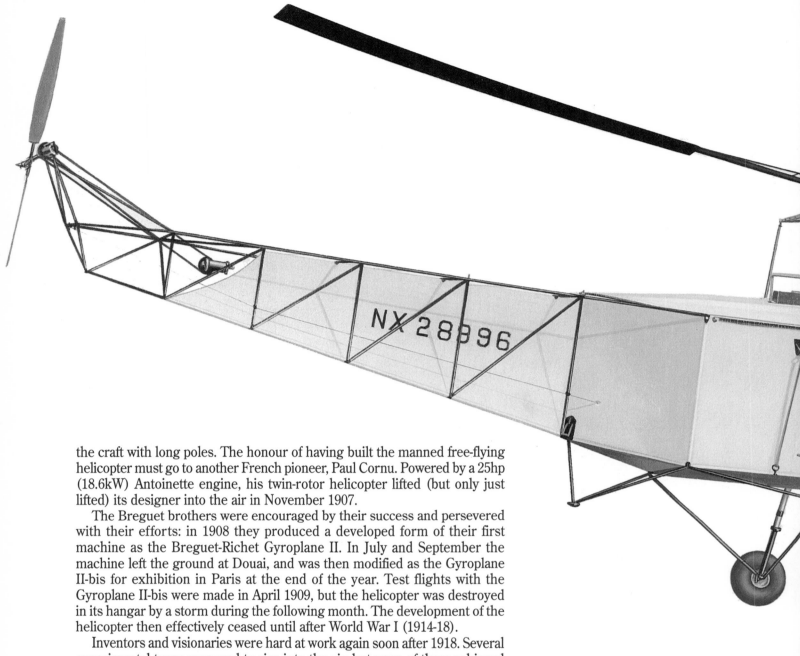

NX 28996

the craft with long poles. The honour of having built the manned free-flying helicopter must go to another French pioneer, Paul Cornu. Powered by a 25hp (18.6kW) Antoinette engine, his twin-rotor helicopter lifted (but only just lifted) its designer into the air in November 1907.

The Breguet brothers were encouraged by their success and persevered with their efforts: in 1908 they produced a developed form of their first machine as the Breguet-Richet Gyroplane II. In July and September the machine left the ground at Douai, and was then modified as the Gyroplane II-bis for exhibition in Paris at the end of the year. Test flights with the Gyroplane II-bis were made in April 1909, but the helicopter was destroyed in its hangar by a storm during the following month. The development of the helicopter then effectively ceased until after World War I (1914-18).

Inventors and visionaries were hard at work again soon after 1918. Several experimental types managed to rise into the air, but none of them achieved anything more than that. It was May 1924 before another French pioneer, Etienne Oehmichen, made the world's first closed-circuit helicopter flight of 0.62 miles (1km) in his four-rotor Oehmichen No.2 machine, at Arlonans. This was an advance, but only a marginal advance, for the problems of control were still formidable.

Incidence and pitch control were at last brought to a practical level by the experiments of an Argentine pioneer, the Marquis Raoul Pateras de Pescara, who produced a series of helicopters in Spain and France between 1919 and 1925. Yet this far-sighted man, whose machines had clearly overcome the main problem of unequal lift, was denied fame by his failure in the matter of torque control. In other respects the Pescara helicopters were good machines, and showed what could be anticipated once full control had been achieved.

Other pioneers active in the early 1920s were the American Henry Berliner, who made a successful hovering flight in 1922 after having considered the

Opposite: The photograph shows Igor Sikorsky himself at the controls of the VS-300 prototype during 1940. This reveals the prototype in its original form with a small enclosed tailboom carrying the anti-torque rotor.

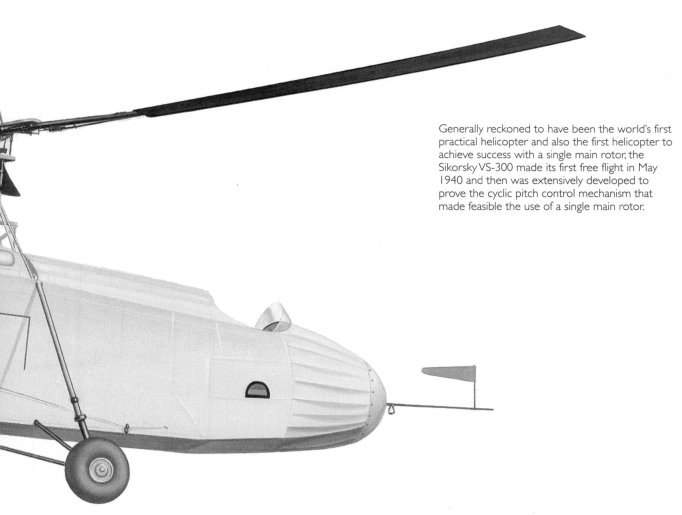

Generally reckoned to have been the world's first practical helicopter and also the first helicopter to achieve success with a single main rotor, the Sikorsky VS-300 made its first free flight in May 1940 and then was extensively developed to prove the cyclic pitch control mechanism that made feasible the use of a single main rotor.

problem since 1905, de Bothezat also in the United States, and Louis Brennan, superintendent of the United Kingdom's torpedo factory during World War I and later head of the rotorcraft department at the Royal Aircraft Establishment at Farnborough. Like Oehmichen, all these men saw their hopes founder on the problems of cyclic pitch control.

The key figure in the development of rotary-wing flight was a Spaniard, Juan de la Cierva. The machine he invented (and patented as the Autogiro) was not a helicopter, however, but rather the gyroplane or, as it later became, the autogyro. In this type of machine, the lifting rotor is unpowered: lift is generated by the freely windmilling overhead rotor as an engine and conventional propeller drive the machine through the air. Most early autogyros had a tractor engine/propeller combination at the front of the aeroplane-type fuselage, while most later autogyros have used a pusher engine/propeller combination at the rear of a fuselage nacelle that also supports the conventional tail unit by means of a boom extending rearward under the propeller. The autogyro depends on forward motion in the air, without which the rotor will stop revolving and the machine will fall, albeit safely with some lift still generated by the freely windmilling rotor.

Cierva's driving passion was the creation of heavier-than-air craft that could not be stalled, as had happened in the fatal crash of his first fixed-wing aeroplane. Cierva's first three Autogiros, the C.1 to C.3 built and tested between 1920 and 1922, failed because of their use of inflexible rotor blades. In 1922, however, Cierva built a model with articulated hinges that permitted the blades to flap: as they rotated the blades were thus free to fall as they retreated at a lower relative speed and rise as they advanced at a higher relative speed, thereby modifying the apparent angle of attack and equalising the amount of lift generated on each side of the rotor. This system was applied to the C.4 Autogiro that made its first successful flight during January 1923. Cierva had understood the full nature of the problem and had found a practical solution to it. The real beauty of the system lay in its simplicity: the blades moved automatically until the whole rotating system was in equilibrium.

Opposite: Another photograph reveals Igor Sikorsky at the controls of the VS-300 prototype during April 1941, after the machine had been revised with a more fully enclosed fuselage and twin-float alighting gear for trials into the helicopter's suitability for waterborne operation.

The Flettner Fl 185 that first flew in 1936 was an overly complex prototype with a single 160hp (119kW) Siemens-Halske Sh.14A radial engine mounted in the nose to drive the overhead rotor, the two anti-torque rotors located on outriggers extending from the sides of the fuselage, and a small fan that helped to cool the engine.

In 1925, Cierva decided to move to the United Kingdom, where he hoped there would be a better market for his Autogiro. The flapping mechanism became very sophisticated in later models, but remained essentially the same as in the C.4, operating entirely automatically and under the influence of purely aerodynamic forces. Although its success gave helicopter designers a clear indication of what they should be looking for, the autogyro system could not be used as it stood: the application of power to the rotor prevented the system from operating automatically.

Cierva enjoyed moderate success as his fully developed Autogiros became popular with both the public and the military. For this he was indebted to the exhibitions and test flights undertaken by his two most important assistants, Harold F. Pitcairn in the United States, and Captain Frank Courtney in the UK. The Autogiro's primary limitation, it should be noted, was its related inability to take-off vertically or to hover motionless in the air. The second aspect did not worry Cierva unduly, but he was determined to find some practical method for allowing vertical take-off, for this would increase the military utility of the Autogiro. Cierva had already introduced a system for spinning the rotor before take-off, thus shortening the ground run, and a pitch-changing mechanism was fitted to Autogiros in the late 1920s to supplement the flapping motion in equalising lift. The final link, a clutch device, was demonstrated in July 1933. Power from the engine at the nose of the fuselage was now taken along a series of shafts through the fuselage and up to the rotor. This was engaged to the drive and was spun to flying speed before lift was allowed to develop, the clutch was

D-EFLT

released, and all the power was applied to the propeller that pulled the machine through the air as soon as the spun-up rotor had lifted it into the air.

In this way the Autogiro could make a jump start into the air, where the propeller provided the forward speed which made the rotor turn on its own. The key to rotor spin-up on the ground was the pitch-control mechanism, which kept the rotor blades at zero incidence, preventing them from generating asymmetric lift until the moment when the clutch was disengaged and the rotor resumed its natural performance. The whole machine 'jumped' some 20ft (6.1m) into the air before the propeller took over.

These Autogiros were a startling sight in operation and proved very successful, continuing in service well into World War II (1939-45). After this time they faded into obscurity until rescued in the 1960s by a wave of enthusiasm for miniature types intended only for sporting use. The main users of Autogiros in World War II were the British, who used the type's ability to stay almost in one spot to help calibrate radar equipment, a function that could not have been undertaken readily by conventional aircraft.

The Germans developed an experimental unpowered autogyro, the Focke-Achgelis Fa 330 Bachstelze, for possible use as an observation platform for U-boats. This simple yet effective little machine could be dismantled into small units for stowage; in operation, the U-boat would tow the Fa 330 at the end of a wire, thus giving it the necessary forward speed for its rotor to windmill and thereby generate lift. From some distance behind and above the parent U-boat the observer in the autogyro enjoyed an excellent field of vision and could search for prey reported to the U-boat via a telephone wire attached to the towing cable. This ingenious and workable system was not used operationally, however, since it meant that the U-boats would stay on the surface for dangerously prolonged periods, and a crash dive would sacrifice the pilot and autogyro as the towing cable was severed.

The success of the Autogiro built by Cierva and his licensees and of the autogyro built by other designers had the fortunate effect of spurring on the development of the helicopter, for here at last was clear proof that rotor-lifted aircraft were practical flying machines. The most important figures in this final stage were Professor Heinrich Focke, one of the parent figures of the

Focke-Wulf company, and the Russian-born Igor Sikorsky, well known before World War I for his giant four-engined aircraft and as the designer and manufacturer of many flying boats and amphibians since emigrating to the USA after the Russian Revolution of 1917.

Focke was the first to achieve any success when his Fw 61 was developed into a production machine. Its maiden flight was in 1936, a year after Breguet had flown the Breguet-Dorand Gyroplane Laboratoire as a successful helicopter using co-axial twin rotors to overcome torque reaction effects. The Breguet helicopter progressed no further, however, leaving the field to Focke and his partner Gerd Achgelis, with whom he had worked in 1932 after leaving Focke-Wulf. Achgelis had been a Focke-Wulf employee and was a superb aerobatic pilot, which was a useful background for learning to handle a new type of aeroplane.

The prototype of the world's first successful helicopter flew in June 1936 and soon proved its worth. Powered by a 160hp (119kW) Bramo (Siemens-Halske) Sh.14A radial piston engine, the Fw 61 was lifted and propelled by a pair of counter-rotating rotors mounted on the ends of two steel-tube outriggers set out from the fuselage based on that of the Focke-Wulf Fw 44 Stieglitz basic training aeroplane. As in the Breguet type but rather more clumsily, the torque reaction of each rotor cancelled that of the other rotor and made the machine directionally stable. The Fw 61 set up some impressive world records for helicopters, including a distance of 143 miles (230km), speed of 76mph (122km/h), endurance of 1 hour 20 minutes 49 seconds, and altitude of 11,243ft (3,427m).

The Fw 61 was fully controllable and thereby proved that helicopters were practical flying machines, but it was only a prototype and therefore lacked the power-to-weight ratio that permitted the carriage of a payload. So the designers decided to refine and lighten their basic concept before producing a production model. Four years passed before the Focke-Achgelis Fa 223 Drache was ready for production in 1940, and even after the type was ordered for German military service, production was hampered by Allied air attacks and only nine production-standard Fa 223s were completed during the war; another three were built after the war from salvaged parts.

Igor Sikorsky became interested in rotary-wing flight during his pioneer period in Russia, and built his first helicopter in 1909: this machine was powered by a 25hp (18.6kW) Anzani engine and would not leave the ground. In 1910, Sikorsky built a second prototype, but although this could rise into the air it was incapable of lifting both itself and a pilot. Realising that rotary-wing aircraft were beyond the capabilities of current technologies, Sikorsky turned his attention to a series of large fixed-wing aircraft, culminating in the Ilya Muromets bomber of 1914 that was the world's first successful four-engined aeroplane. After the Bolshevik Revolution of 1917 that turned Russia into the USSR, Sikorsky left the country and settled in the USA during 1919, turning his attention to the design of flying boats and amphibians. Sikorsky rose to the position of engineering manager of the Vought-Sikorsky Division of the United Aircraft Corporation, and in 1938 he decided to capitalise on years of reflection by addressing the problems of rotary-wing flight.

Receiving authorisation to proceed with the design and construction of a helicopter prototype, Sikorsky produced the VS-300 that first flew in tethered mode during September 1939 with a 75hp (55.9kW) Lycoming air-cooled radial piston engine. The VS-300 underwent a major development programme, and made its first free flight in May 1940 with a Franklin engine rated at 90hp (67.1kW). The VS-300 became the world's first truly practical helicopter of

The Flettner Fl 282 Kolibri (humming bird) was one of the most advanced helicopters designed in World War II, and its use of closely spaced intermeshing twin-rotors produced a compact design that appealed most strongly to the German navy for shipboard applications. The Fl 282 was powered by a 160hp (119kW) Bramo (Siemens-Halske) Sh.14A radial piston engine, and its primary data included rotor diameters of 39ft 2.875in (11.96m), fuselage length of 21ft 6.25in (6.56m), height of 7ft 2.625in (2.20m), maximum take-off weight of 2,205lb (1,000kg), maximum speed of 93mph (150km/h) at sea level, service ceiling of 10,825ft (3,300m), and range of 106 miles (170km).

the single main rotor type in December 1941, when it was flown successfully as the VS-300A with the definitive cyclic pitch control system (developed to practical status by Landgraf) and a single anti-torque tail rotor. Testing and development continued through 1942 with power increased to 150hp (112kW) to create the final VS-300B form, and this epoch-making helicopter was retired to the Henry Ford Museum in 1943. Whereas the Breguet-Dorand and Fw 61 must be reckoned to have been the world's first successful helicopters, in that they could take-off and land vertically, and undertake forward, backward and sideways manoeuvres in the air, the VS-300 must similarly be reckoned as the world's first practical helicopter as it combined these features with the factor that allowed its development into a production type also capable of carrying a payload.

Although the type was planned for large-scale production, the Flettner Fl 282 Kolibri was in fact produced only in prototype and pre-production models for the evaluation of its technical and operational capabilities. This model is typical of the type as trialled for the observation role, with a Plexiglas-covered forward fuselage providing good fields of vision.

Impressed with the potential of the VS-300, the US Army Air Corps (known as the US Army Air Forces (USAAF) later that year) had contracted in the spring of 1941 for an improved experimental type with two-seat accommodation. This VS-316A was evolved as a development of the VS-300A/B, retaining the earlier type's heavy-gauge steel-tube fuselage structure with all except the extreme tail covered in fabric, but featuring a powerplant of one 165hp (123kW) Warner R-500-3 radial piston engine driving a fabric-covered three-blade main rotor via a gearbox that turned the drive angle through 90 degrees, enclosed side-by-side accommodation with side doors and optional dual controls, and fixed tailwheel landing gear whose main wheels could be replaced by two inflated rubber pontoons for amphibious capability. This prototype first flew in May 1942 as the XR-4, and was followed by another 30 helicopters for service trials. These were three YR-4A and 27 improved YR-4B machines (including three diverted to the US Navy with the designation HNS-1), with a main rotor whose diameter was increased from the XR-4's figure of 36ft 0in (10.97m) to 38ft 0in (11.58m) and driven by the more powerful 180hp (134kW) Warner R-550-1 engine.

These machines proved the practical nature of the helicopter in trials as diverse as arctic operations and maritime capability from a platform on an oil tanker. There followed an initial production batch of 100 R-4B helicopters delivered in 1944: 20 of these were diverted to the US Navy for use by the US Coast Guard with the designation HNS-1, and 45 were transferred to the Royal Air Force (RAF) and Fleet Air Arm (FAA) with the designation Hoverfly Mk I that was also applied to seven YR-4Bs transferred to the UK. In 1948, the helicopters still operational with the new US Air Force (USAF), as the USAAF had become in 1947, were allocated the revised designation H-4B, signalling the change from the R-for-Rotary wing to H-for-Helicopter category.

The USAAF never considered the R-4 as anything other than a trials type that could explore both the practicality and utility of the helicopter in military service, and this limited expectation of the type was justified by the type's service life, which revealed only marginal capabilities with two men on board. What was needed was a more powerful version of the same basic type, and this was ordered in 1942 as the R-5 that was designed as the VS-327. While this new type was being developed and prepared for production, the USAAF decided that it needed a refined version of the R-4 for continued examination of the helicopter's capabilities. Ordered in 1943 as the R-6, this was designed as the VS-316B to reflect the fact that the type was essentially an improved VS-316A with the same rotor and transmission systems but powered by the 225hp (168kW) Lycoming O-435-7 flat-six piston engine. The fuselage was completely revised into the tadpole type that became typical of Sikorsky helicopters of the next generation: this had a formed Plexiglas cockpit section and a metal semi-monocoque boom to support the anti-torque tail rotor.

The XR-6 prototype first flew in October 1943, and in March 1944 established impressive world helicopter altitude, distance and endurance records during the course of non-stop flight between Washington, DC and Dayton, Ohio, in which the machine covered 387 miles (623km) in 4 hours 55 minutes, with an altitude of 5,000ft (1,525m) recorded during the crossing of the Allegheny mountains. There followed 31 service test and development helicopters each powered by the 240hp (179kW) Franklin O-405-9 flat-six piston engine: these were five XR-6A and 26 YR-6A helicopters built respectively by Sikorsky and Nash-Kelvinator. The latter won the contract for 193 R-6A production machines. Production started in 1945, and it is uncertain whether or not the full total was completed. Some 36 of the helicopters were diverted with the designation HOS-1 to the US Navy, which used the type for the search-and-rescue (SAR) role and also received three XH-6As with the revised designation XHOS-1, and another 26 were delivered to the UK for use by the RAF and FAA with the designation Hoverfly Mk II.

The R-6A was beset by engine problems, but the helicopters that survived to 1948 received the revised designation H-6A.

In 1942 the USAAF decided that the helicopter had considerable potential as an air observation post machine, but only if it provided better payload and performance than the R-4. To meet the resulting requirement, Sikorsky designed the VS-327 as a conceptual offspring of the R-4, although it was a completely new design and introduced a number of features that were soon to become standard on early Sikorsky helicopters. The core of the new design was the powerplant, which comprised a 450hp (336kW) Pratt & Whitney R-985 radial piston engine located with its crankshaft vertical to drive a much larger main rotor via a clutch and cooling fan arrangement. The central fuselage carried the engine and was of welded steel-tube construction covered with resin-bonded shaped plywood panels rather than fabric as in the R-4, the slim forward fuselage carried the crew of two (observer in front of the

The Focke-Achgelis Fa 223 Drache (kite) was a large helicopter that adhered to the design concept pioneered in the Fa 61 with two large counter-rotating propellers at the tips of the fuselage-mounted outriggers. The Fa 223 was powered by a 1,000hp (746kW) Bramo 323Q03 radial piston engine, and its other details included rotor diameters of 39ft 4.5in (12.00m), overall span of 80ft 4.625in (24.50m), fuselage length of 40ft 2.25in (12.25m), height of 15ft 9in (4.80m), maximum take-off weight of 9,500lb (4,315kg), maximum speed of 75mph (120.5km/h) at sea level, service ceiling of 23,295ft (7,100m), and range of 199 miles (320km).

Built in the UK under licence from Cierva, the Avro Rota Mk I was an Autogiro used in modest numbers by the Royal Air Force before and during World War II. The key features of the design were an aeroplane-type fuselage with a 140hp (104kW) Armstrong Siddeley Genet Major radial piston engine located in the nose and driving a tractor propeller, wide-track main landing gear units, a substantial tail unit, and an unpowered three-blade rotor carried above the fuselage on a substantial quadruped pylon. The details of this useful type included a rotor diameter of 37ft 0in (11.28m), fuselage length of 19ft 8.5in (6.01m), height of 11ft 1in (3.38m), maximum take-off weight of 1,900lb (862kg), maximum speed of 110mph (177km/h) at sea level, service ceiling of 8,000ft (2,440m), and range of 250 miles (402km).

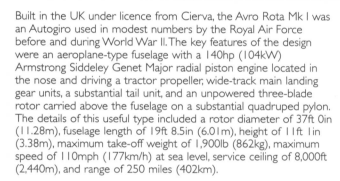

19

Rotor Control

THE main problem encountered in early helicopters was the tendency of the machine to roll laterally in the direction of the retreating rotor blades as the advancing blades passed through more air and generated greater lift than the retreating blades that passed through less air. This problem was eventually solved by the introduction of a flapping hinge in the rotor head, which allowed the advancing blade to climb slightly, thereby reducing its angle of attack and the amount of lift generated, while the retreating blade fell slightly, thereby increasing its angle of attack and the amount of lift generated, so that the turning rotor blades generated an equal amount of lift on each side of the shaft. The other two main features of the helicopter's control system, which are operated by the pilot, are the collective and cyclic pitch controls. The collective pitch control is the method by which the pilot controls the helicopter's ascent and descent by the increase or decrease simultaneously (i.e. collectively) of the pitch angle of all the main rotor blades, thereby increasing or decreasing the amount of lift generated by the whole of the rotor disc. The cyclic pitch control is the method by which the pilot controls the helicopter's direction in level flight by altering the pitch angle of each main rotor blade consecutively (i.e. cyclically) at a given geometric position in each revolution, thereby tilting the main rotor disc's theoretical axis of rotation in the desired direction; to tilt the rotor disc forward to create forward motion from the hover, for example, the pitch angle of each advancing blade is reduced and that of each retreating blade increased.

pilot) in an extensively glazed metal monocoque structure, and the boom was a wooden monocoque structure. The landing gear was of the fixed type in a reversed tricycle arrangement with the main units well forward and the stalky rear unit located at the junction of the central fuselage and boom sections.

The USAAF ordered an eventual five prototypes in 1943, and the first of these XR-5 helicopters flew in August 1943 with the R-985-AN-5 engine; two of the prototypes were later retrofitted to British specification and received the revised designation XR-5A. There followed 26 examples of the YR-5A service test type of which two were diverted to the US Navy with the designation HO2S-1, and in 1948 the surviving helicopters were allocated the revised designation YH-5A; five of the YR-5As were modified with dual controls with the designation YR-5E that was changed to YH-5E during 1948. The USAAF also ordered 100 examples of the R-5A (from 1948 H-5A) production model, but in the event only 34 were built with provision for a litter carrier on each side of the fuselage.

Some 21 of these helicopters were later modified to R-5D (from 1948 H-5D) standard with internal accommodation for a second passenger, a rescue hoist, conventional tricycle landing gear, a powerplant of one 600hp (447kW) Pratt & Whitney R-1340 radial piston engine, and provision for auxiliary fuel in an external tank. Intended primarily for the civil market, the S-51 model was a development of the R-5D with the R-985 Twin Wasp engine and accommodation for a pilot and up to four passengers. The type first flew in February 1946 and received civil certification during March of the same year, paving the way for deliveries to start in August. In 1947 the new USAF received 11 S-51 helicopters with the service designation R-5F (from 1948 H-5F), and followed in 1948-49 with 39 examples of the H-5G variant equipped with power-boosted controls, untapered rotor blades and a rescue hoist for the SAR role, together with 16 examples of the H-5H variant with updated equipment and provision for pontoon alighting gear in place of the standard wheeled landing gear.

The USAF allocated most of its helicopters to the Air Rescue Service, which flew the type extensively during the Korean War (1950-53) with an enclosed litter carrier on each side of the fuselage. The same basic type was used by the US Navy for the planeguard and general observation roles, and deliveries amounted to some 97 machines. The more important of these models was the HO3S-1 of which 88 were built for delivery from November 1947 and for full service from May 1948. Nine similar aircraft were procured on behalf of the US Coast Guard, which allocated the designation HO3S-1G to the type in the SAR role. A number of other S-51s were delivered to the air arms of other countries.

The most important aspect of the fully developed VS-300 and its Sikorsky successors was the cyclic pitch control, perfected by Landgraf and first fitted in definitive form during December 1941. This now became the heart of the helicopter in every form, and many forms of helicopter were tried successfully during the 1940s. In the USA, Kellett, who had previously produced autogyros, developed a helicopter with counter-rotating twin rotors, set on angled shafts so that the blades intermeshed, helping to reduce the overall 'span'.

Friedrich von Doblhoff, an Austrian, made his mark with the first jet-propelled helicopter, the Doblhoff WNF 342. This introduced the unusual concept of feeding compressed air and fuel into combustion chambers at the tips of the rotor blades, where the vapour mixture was burned to provide thrust. The generation of power at the rotor tips rather than in the fuselage avoided torque problems and made the tail rotor unnecessary. Experimental models with this sort of propulsion have been tested ever since, but despite its clear advantages the type has never found favour. Another major contender within the German Reich was Anton Flettner, with the Flettner Fl 282 Kolibri. Flettner remains one of the lesser known pioneers of rotary-wing flight, which is remarkable given the fact that his first fully practical helicopter, the Fl 265, was superior to the Fw 61 and made its first successful free flight several months before the VS-300 began its initial tethered flights. Flettner had been a devotee of rotary-wing flight since the early 1930s, and was particularly anxious to overcome the torque-reaction problem associated with a lifting rotor driven by a fuselage-mounted engine. This preoccupation was evident in Flettner's first helicopter design, completed in 1930, which was based on a large two-blade rotor powered directly by two Anzani piston engines, each rated at 30hp (22.4kW) and installed on one of the rotor blades to drive a small tractor propeller.

The prototype of this helicopter was overturned by a gust of wind and destroyed during 1933 in the course of tethered trials. Flettner then designed a two-seat autogyro as the Fl 184 with enclosed two-seat accommodation, fixed tailwheel landing gear with cantilever main units, a three-blade rotor fitted with a cyclic pitch control system, and a powerplant of one 140hp (104kW) Sh.14 radial piston engine located in the nose to drive a two-blade tractor propeller. This machine was also built in prototype form, but was lost in 1936 after suffering an inflight engine fire. The talented Flettner now turned to the Fl 185 design that was intended to operate as a helicopter when the rotor was powered for vertical flight and as an autogyro when the rotor was unpowered in horizontal flight: the Fl 185 had fixed tricycle landing gear, a three-blade rotor, and a powerplant of one Sh.14A engine. The powerplant was nose-mounted inside a long-chord cowling and drove a frontal cooling fan as well as a gearbox that drove the rotor and/or

Seen here on the production line, the Sikorsky R-4 was developed as the VS-316A (first flight in January 1942) and was the primary definitive evolution of the concepts first embodied in the VS-300, and as such was the first helicopter in the world to enter full-scale production, as the German Fa 223 Drache and Fl 282 Kolibri helicopters had failed to reach this stage. The R-4 introduced fully enclosed accommodation and dual controls for the two-man crew.

two variable-pitch propellers mounted at the tips of outriggers extending from each side of the fuselage: when the rotor was powered, the propellers provided thrust in the opposite direction to counteract the torque reaction, but when the rotor was unpowered, the propellers absorbed the full power of the engine to provide forward thrust. The Fl 185 made only a few test flights before being scrapped.

By this time, however, Flettner had come to his definitive concept of how to obviate torque reaction, namely a side-by-side pair of intermeshing two-blade rotors that were mounted at the heads of two outward-inclined drive shafts and turned in opposite directions so that the torque reaction of one cancelled that of the other. Flettner appreciated that this system would produce a seriously turbulent airflow pattern, but felt that the problems associated with this airflow would be more than offset by the advantages of the torqueless rotor system and the reduced drag that would result from a design that ob-viated the need for any external rotor-carrying structure. The new rotor system was first used on the Fl 265, of which the German navy ordered six prototypes in 1938. The fuselage of the Fl 265 was based on that of the Fl 185 but revised with the intermeshing rotor system and without the two propeller outriggers. The same type of powerplant arrangement was used and, to improve the helicopter's controllability, a conventional tail unit was provided with a trimmable tailplane, and a large vertical tail surface incorporating a rudder was used to supplement the directional control provided by differential collective-pitch change in the two rotors. The Fl 265 V1 first prototype made its maiden flight in May 1939 and, despite its loss a mere three months later when the rotor blades struck each other, soon proved the general success of Flettner's design concept. The five other prototypes were used for a number of successful trials in several military applications, and in 1940 the German navy ordered Flettner to initiate full production of the type. By that time, Flettner had moved forward to a more advanced design and the production order was switched to this more capable type, namely the Fl 282 Kolibri. This was designed as a two-seater so that, at the expense of range, an observer could be carried in a rearward-facing seat that was installed behind the rotor assembly. The design was created with sufficient range in the permissible centre of gravity position so that the helicopter could be flown as a single- or two-seater without trim changes, and its most obvious role was observation in land and naval applications.

The design was completed in July 1940 and work started immediately on no fewer than 30 prototype and 15 pre-production helicopters. Flight trials were scheduled to begin in 1941, and while the first three machines were completed as single-seaters with accommodation for the pilot in an enclosed cockpit, the others were finished as two-seaters with open accommodation. The Fl 282 marked a departure from previous Flettner practice in the location of the Sh.14A engine, which was installed in the centre of the fuselage with a wooden cooling fan that drew air through slots in the underside of the fuselage, and drove a forward-mounted transmission unit that turned the drive through 155 degrees to a 65-degree upward and backward angle to power, via a transmission shaft, the upper transmission unit that drove the two rotor shafts. The latter were inclined outward at 12 degrees and forward at 6 degrees, and carried the two rotors. These were each of the two-blade type, each blade having a steel spar, wooden ribs, and a skinning of plywood covered in fabric: each blade was attached to its rotor hub by flap and drag hinges. The fuselage was of welded steel-tube construction covered over its central portion by light alloy panels and over its rear section by fabric, and carried at its rear the conventional tail unit, which comprised a trimmable horizontal surface and a large vertical surface with a rudder to supplement differential collective-pitch change of the two rotors for directional control. The pilot was accommodated in an open steel-tube structure at the extreme nose, and the airframe was completed by the fixed tricycle landing gear with a single wheel on each unit. The Fl 282 V1 first prototype flew in 1941, and as additional machines became available and the pace of the development programme was accelerated, the Fl 282 soon proved itself to be an admirable helicopter that combined great reliability with viceless handling characteristics.

Operational trials were undertaken from 1942, and so useful was the Fl 282 that, from 1943, about 20 of the 24 completed development helicopters were used for the convoy escort role in the Mediterranean and Black Seas. In 1944 the German air ministry ordered 1,000 production examples of the Fl 282 from BMW, but no production helicopters were completed as a result of the programme's dislocation by Allied bombing. Only three of the Fl 282 helicopters survived to VE-Day in May 1945, many of the others having been destroyed to prevent their capture by the Allies.

The other major American pioneer of the single-rotor helicopter was Bell. During World War II, Bell cut its rotary-wing teeth on the Model 30 design, of which five were built as research helicopters. From the third of these machines the company developed the Model 47 as a practical helicopter paving the way for a production model. The first of 11 prototype and service test helicopters flew in December 1945 with an open fuselage structure, quadricycle landing gear, and a powerplant of one 175hp (130.5kW) Franklin horizontally opposed piston engine, and in March 1946 the Model 47 became the first helicopter in the world to receive civil certification.

This was the first of 27 Sikorsky YR-4B helicopters built to a contract issued by the US Army Air Forces for evaluation machines that were operated by the USAAF, US Navy and Royal Air Force to the extent of 17, three and seven machines respectively. The YR-4B was powered by a 180hp (134kW) Warner R-550-1 radial piston engine driving a main rotor with a diameter of 38ft 0in (11.58m), and also had a larger cockpit than that of the initial XR-4 and YR-4A machines, of which one and three respectively were built. The XR-4 was powered by a 165hp (134kW) Warner R-500-1 radial engine driving a main rotor with a diameter of 36ft 0in (10.97m), but a larger engine and rotor were introduced on the YR-4As. The YR-4Bs were used for trials under arctic and tropical conditions, and it was a YR-4B that undertook the first helicopter evacuation of a wounded soldier, an event that took place in Burma during 1944.

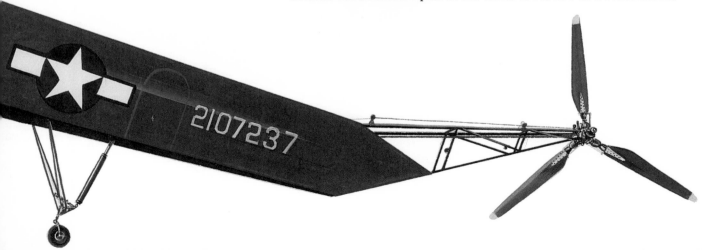

The first production version was the two-seat Model 47B, of which 78 were completed with the 175hp (130.5kW) Franklin 6ALV-335 engine. There followed a number of mainly civil Model 47 variants that also secured orders with an increasing number of the world's air arms. The most important of these were the Model 47D with the Franklin 6V4-178-B32 engine rated at 178hp (133kW) and a blown Plexiglas canopy in place of the Model 47B's car-type windscreen; the definitive three-seat Model 47G with the 200hp (149kW) Franklin 6V4-200-C32AB engine and a small horizontal tailplane at the tail; and the four-seat Model 47J Ranger with the 220hp (164kW) Lycoming VO-435 flat-six piston engine. The Model 47G and Model 47J were built respectively in 10 and six subvariants, distinguishable by their different engines.

The Model 47 soon attracted the attention of the USAAF, which saw the type as a useful utility helicopter, and in 1947 the service received 28 Model 47A helicopters with the 175hp (130.5kW) Franklin O-335-1 engine for evaluation under the designation YR-13. Ten of the helicopters were diverted to the US Navy, and three of them were modified to YR-13A standard suitable for operation in cold climates.

The first full production order was placed by the US Army, which in 1948 contracted for 65 examples of a Model 47D variant for service under the H-13B designation with the 200hp (149kW) Franklin O-335-3 engine and a bubble canopy with a removable top. The 15 H-13C helicopters were H-13Bs stripped of their rear fuselage covering and revised with twin-skid landing gear for use in the casevac role, with a litter pannier carried externally on each side of the fuselage. The H-13D military version of the model 47D-1, of which 87 were delivered, had single rather than dual controls, skid landing gear, and the 200hp (149kW) O-335-5 engine, and in 1962 the surviving helicopters were redesignated OH-13D in the rationalisation of the US tri-service designation system. Some 490 of the H-13E derivative of the H-13D

A type that saw limited operational use as a means of increasing the spotting horizon for U-boats, the Focke-Achgelis Fa 330 Bachstelze (water wagtail) was a kite autogyro towed to spotting height by a moving submarine. The type's primary details included a rotor diameter of 24ft 0in (7.315m), fuselage length of 14ft 6in (4.42m), empty weight of 180lb (82kg), and a minimum air speed of 17mph (27km/h) to maintain flight.

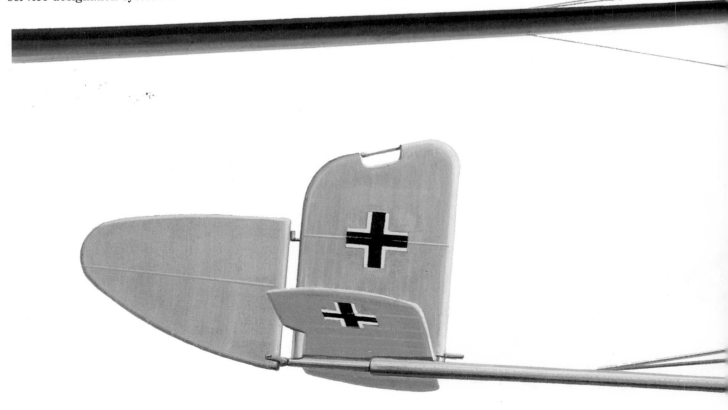

were delivered with dual controls, three seats, a new main transmission and tail, and the 200hp (149kW) O-335-5B engine, and in 1962 the surviving helicopters were redesignated OH-13E Sioux. More than 260 of the H-13G military derivative of the Model 47G were delivered with a controllable stabilizer, relocated and larger fuel tankage, a number of stability-enhancing features, provision for two external litter panniers, and the 200hp (149kW) Lycoming VO-435 engine, and in 1962 the surviving helicopters were redesignated H-13G. Some 470 of the H-47H military derivative of the Model 47G-2 were delivered with dual controls, provision for two external litter panniers, revised skid landing gear, bonded all-metal rotor blades, and the 250hp (186kW) VO-435-23 engine, and in 1962 the surviving helicopters were redesignated OH-13H. The H-13J, of which just two were delivered, was a three-seat presidential transport derivative of the Model 47J with more comfortable accommodation and the 240hp (179kW) VO-435-21 engine, and in 1962 the helicopters were redesignated UH-13J. The OH-13S, of which 265 were delivered to succeed the H-13H, was the military derivative of the Model 47G-3B with the tail boom lengthened by 1ft 2in (0.356m), main rotor blades extended by 1ft 0in (0.305m), and power provided by the 260hp (194kW) TVO-435-25 engine. The TH-13T military derivative of the Model

25

47G-3B-1, of which 411 were delivered for the instrument training role, featured considerably more advanced avionics than earlier models, the cabin was widened by 8in (0.203m) by comparison with that of the OH-13S, and power was provided by the 270hp (201kW) TVO-435-25 engine.

The US Navy also appreciated the potential of the Model 47 as a helicopter trainer, and evaluated the basic type's capabilities in the form of 10 YR-13 helicopters transferred with the naval designation HTL-1. The service followed with an order for 12 of the HTL-2 version of the Model 47D, and later orders added variants up to the HTL-7. The US Navy also perceived the Model 47's application in the utility and icebreaker patrol roles, and 28 of the HUL-1 naval derivative of the Model 47J variant were delivered, the surviving helicopters being redesignated UH-13P in 1962. Two HUL-1s diverted to the US Coast Guard for the SAR role in arctic conditions were designated HUL-1G, and in 1962 the helicopters were redesignated HH-13Q.

The Model 47 was built extensively under licence in Italy by Agusta, in Japan by Kawasaki and in the UK, under sub-licence from Agusta, by Westland. Large-scale production of the Model 47 in all its military and civil variants lasted from 1945 to the 1980s and resulted in several thousands of civil and military helicopters in a bewildering number of variants with open and enclosed cockpits and steadily increasing engine power. The Model 47 proved especially useful in urban areas and for various types of short-range flying. It was not long before the implications of the helicopter's independence from specially constructed landing sites became clear. New buildings began to feature landing pads on their roofs, and police departments realised that the helicopter, with its slow flying speed and ever-increasing endurance, was ideally suited for traffic surveillance and similar activities.

The helicopter's only major drawback in an urban environment has been its noisiness. At first this was not an acute problem, for the smaller engines used in the early 1950s were relatively quiet and the public was less concerned about the environment. But the growing size and increasing weight of helicopters required the use of more powerful and consequently noisier engines. At the same time, improvements to both control and rotors allowed the helicopter to undertake a wider variety of roles with an increasingly heavy payload. This tendency was further increased by the development of a turbine engine suitable for helicopter installations. This is the turboshaft, which has a considerably higher power-to-weight ratio than the radial piston engine. In itself this has improved the helicopter's payload capability, but other important advantages of a turboshaft powerplant are greater fuel economy, relatively vibration-free running, increased reliability, reduced volume, and lighter weight. These last two factors have been particularly important, for they opened the way for the powerplant to be relocated from the fuselage to a position above the cabin and close to the rotor shaft: this made greater fuselage volume available for payload, and also resulted in a further lightening of the dynamic system by removing the need for long transmission shafts connecting any fuselage-mounted engine with the gearbox located at the base of the rotor shaft.

The USA had pioneered the practical helicopter, and this allowed American companies other than Sikorsky and Bell (most notably Hiller, Hughes, Kaman, Piasecki and Vertol) to develop a thriving international business as well as excellent sales within the USA. Vertol (later Boeing-Vertol and now Boeing Helicopters), Piasecki and Kaman concentrated on particular designs of twin-rotor helicopters, the first two on long-bodied machines with counter-rotating rotors at each end of the fuselage, and the last on short stumpy designs with an intermeshing arrangement of counter-rotating rotors.

By the 1950s, several European companies had entered the arena of helicopter design and manufacture. Westland, Saunders-Roe and Bristol were early leaders in the UK, but by the 1960s, Westland, licence-holders for Sikorsky designs, had achieved dominance. Sud-Est (later part of Aérospatiale) took most of the market in France, Bölkow (later MBB, now part of Eurocopter) led the field in Germany, and Agusta was dominant in Italy. Perversely, as the number of aircraft manufacturers declined in the 1960s and 1970s, that of helicopter manufacturers increased, especially in Latin America and Japan, although many of these produced only a few machines or just a single type before fading into obscurity.

The Mil design bureau achieved a virtual monopoly in the USSR, now the Commonwealth of Independent States (CIS), with some outstanding designs in several categories of medium single-rotor and heavy twin-rotor machines. The most important designer of naval helicopters, however, has been the Kamov bureau, which concentrates on helicopters of compact design through the use of a co-axial arrangement of two contra-rotating rotors.

Helicopter Types

In the course of a life now amounting to some 60 years, the helicopter has been developed in a number of forms offering particular advantages and disadvantages. The first helicopters used a pair of contra-rotating rotors arranged on outriggers extended from the fuselage and generally used to support the main landing gear units. The primary advantage of this system, as first displayed in the Focke-Achgelis Fa 61, is the fact that it removes the need for an anti-torque rotor at the tail and permits the use of two simple rotors without complex hinges and controls; the primary disadvantage is the overall width. The width factor was tackled and overcome in helicopters such as the Flettner Fl 282 with the counter-rotating rotors installed on masts located close to each other but inclined slightly outward, so that the two rotor discs could intermesh without the blades touching. The definitive expression of two closely spaced main rotors is found in the helicopters of Nikolai Kamov, who adopted contra-rotating rotors with one installed above the other in a co-axial fashion so that the torque reaction of each rotor is cancelled by that of the other, and this allowed the creation of notably compact helicopters well suited to shipboard applications. The other main employment of two main rotors is in the tandem-rotor system in which the two counter-rotating rotors are located at the forward and rear ends of a longer fuselage with the rear rotor located above the front unit. Helicopters of this type were designed by Bristol, Yakovlev and Piasecki, the last's types being the most successful, as the company became known as Vertol that eventually became part of Boeing and is still responsible for the Model 107 and Model 114 series that are in service as the H-46 Sea Knight and H-47 Chinook series respectively. The primary advantage of the tandem-rotor layout is the ability to lift heavy loads whose position relative to the helicopter's centre of gravity is less critical than in single-rotor designs. This leaves the 'standard' helicopter pioneered by Sikorsky with a single main rotor whose torque reaction is controlled by a small rotor (or now the lateral expulsion of engine exhaust gases) at the tail.

The Boeing CH-47 Chinook is typical of the modern tandem-rotor transport helicopter: the long fuselage has a rectangular-section cabin accessed by a ventral ramp/door arrangement for the carriage of anything from troops to light vehicles, provision under the fuselage for the lifting of external loads on a three-point lift system, fuel carried in the external pannier tanks to leave the fuselage free for payload, landing gear of the quadricycle type for great stability on the ground, and the twin-rotor dynamic system that provides great lifting capability and also gives great flexibility in the centre of gravity position. The rotor system is based on two three-blade rotors indexed at 30 degrees to each other so that their blades can intermesh in the longitudinal plane without touching, and these rotors are powered by two turboshafts installed in nacelles on the sides of the pylon carrying the rear rotor and driving a transmission system that allows either engine to drive both rotors.

From Piston to Turbine Power

THE most striking attribute of the helicopter is its versatility, a capability appreciable from the mid-1950s after the adoption of the turboshaft in place of the air-cooled piston engine as the standard type of powerplant in all but the lightest helicopters. Some helicopters were built for specific roles, but most of them proved able to undertake other tasks, especially as the power-to-weight ratio of the helicopter had been improved with the introduction of turboshaft engines. Moreover, in contrast to aircraft built since the end of World War II, many civilian and military helicopters have been evolved on the basis of a common airframe and rotor system. This factor resulted mainly from the fact that, up to the late 1960s, the helicopter was intended mainly as a transport vehicle.

While the basic helicopter could carry passengers on a commercial basis for civilian operators, it could also be adapted for use as an anti-submarine weapon, an SAR or air-sea rescue type, or a heavy-lift machine by adding the relevant equipment. This adaptation made economic sense, and was entirely feasible before helicopters were streamlined for operations in a hostile environment. This development occurred in the late 1960s when the helicopter's success in the Vietnam War combined with new technology and design ideas to foster a division between civil and military machines.

After the United States, the USSR was the next major power to produce a helicopter of its own design. The Mil Mi-1 'Hare' entered production in 1948 as a light transport type, but was soon supplanted by the Mi-2 'Hoplite' that was also built in large numbers. A year later the American, Stanley Hiller, introduced his Hiller 12 series of light utility helicopters, of which eventually more than 2,000 were built. Helicopters as small as these represented the only early designs which could not readily be adapted for other uses, as their payloads were so small. Training, observation and light communications were the only tasks that could be undertaken with any real efficiency.

The helicopter thus began to come into its own only during the early 1950s, partly as a result of the celebrated successes of American 'choppers' in Korea. New production facilities were built in other countries and numerous helicopter designs appeared in the first half of the decade. Sud-Est, a French nationalised group, produced its first model in 1951. A utility helicopter, the Alouette (lark) then proved outstandingly successful and the most versatile helicopter of French design. Production variants were the Alouette II and enlarged Alouette III which were each developed in variants with the Turbomeca Artouste and later the Turbomeca Astazou turboshafts.

The Sikorsky S-55 entered service with the US Air Force as the H-19, the US Army as the H-19 Chickasaw, the US Navy as the HO4S and the US Marine Corps as the HRS, and introduced the definitive form of the Sikorsky concept of piston-engined single-rotor helicopters for utility employment. The features that contribute to this 'definitive' nature included quadricycle landing gear, a 'pod-and-boom' fuselage with the high-set boom supported by a triangular fillet and the pod optimised for the transport role with considerable internal capacity and sliding lateral doors, the high-set cockpit, and the radial piston engine located low in the extreme nose to drive the rotor system via a long transmission shaft extending obliquely backward and upward to the main gearbox.

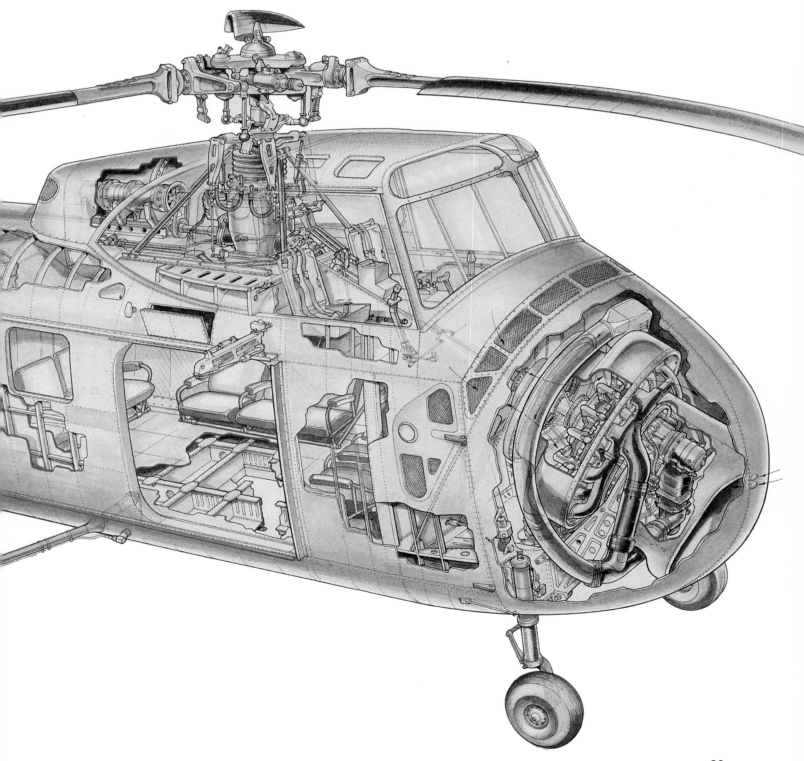

The Yakovlev Yak-24 'Horse' appeared in the same year, and was the world's largest helicopter at the time. Intended as a military transport, the Yak-24 set a number of world rotorcraft records but was built only in small numbers because of intractable handling problems.

In 1952, Mikhail Mil designed a large helicopter that was clearly inspired by the Sikorsky S-55 of 1949. Built over a period of more than 10 years by the parent company to the extent of 1,281 helicopters for the civil and military markets, the S-55 was the first Sikorsky helicopter to be built in very large numbers, and the production total was swelled beyond the American figure by licensed construction in France (five helicopters built by Sud-Est), Japan (71 machines built by Mitsubishi) and the UK (485 examples of the somewhat different Westland Whirlwind as an improved version of the baseline model).

The origins of the S-55 can be traced back to the technical success of the VS-327 built for the US forces as the R-5 (later H-5), and the S-51 series produced for the USAF and US Navy as the H-5 (later models) and HO3S respectively. This basic model had proved that the helicopter was a practical machine for military use, but also revealed that genuine utility required greater payload through the adoption of a larger airframe that would need a larger main rotor driven by a considerably more powerful engine. Sikorsky evolved such a type as the S-55, and rightly reasoned that the only place to locate the hold was under the main rotor, where changes in payload would not adversely affect the helicopter's centre of gravity position. The hold was accessed by a large starboard-side sliding door, and was planned with a length of 10ft 0in (3.05m), width of 5ft 3in (1.60m) and height of 6ft 0in (1.83m): this meant that unless the fuselage was to be lengthened to a significant degree, the cockpit had to be located above rather than ahead of

Opposite: Piston-engined light helicopters such as the Bell Model 447, seen here in military form as the H-13G, came into their own during the early 1950s for tasks such as observation, liaison and, as is apparent here, casualty evacuation with one or two wounded men loaded onto panniers attached to the sides of the helicopter for rapid evacuation to medical facilities more comprehensive than those on the front line.

Below: The Sikorsky S-51 series was widely used by American allies, this being a helicopter of the series in service with the Royal Canadian navy.

the hold. Because the hold was located on the centre of gravity, it was impossible to install the voluminous and weighty radial piston engine in the same place and, given the choice of positions fore or aft of the hold, the Sikorsky design team opted for a nose installation.

This allowed the engine to be fitted inside large clamshell doors that provided good access for maintenance, but demanded that the rotor system be driven via a long and heavy transmission shaft running obliquely to the gearbox immediately under the main rotor. The fuel tankage was placed below the hold, and the design of the S-55's fuselage was completed by a circular-section boom (installed at right angles to the rear face of the hold) for the anti-torque tail rotor, and by fixed quadricycle landing gear with a single wheel on each unit; twin metal or inflated rubber pontoons could be fitted in place of the wheels for amphibious capability, and there was also provision for the wheeled landing gear units to be fitted with inflatable pontoons for flotation in the event of a ditching. The rotor system comprised a three-blade main rotor and a two-blade tail rotor.

Impressed with the payload-carrying potential of the S-55, the USAF ordered five YH-19 prototypes for evaluation, and the first of these flew in November 1949 with a powerplant of one 550hp (410kW) Pratt & Whitney R-1340 radial piston engine. The second prototype introduced a large triangular fillet in the angle between the rear of the hold section and the underside of the boom, and this became standard on all subsequent helicopters of the family. The type entered production as the S-55A, with a powerplant of one 600hp (447kW) R-1340-57 radial piston engine.

The primary variants of the S-55A initial production model for the US forces were 50 examples of the H-19A for the USAF in the utility role; 72 examples of the H-19C Chickasaw for the US Army in the transport role; 10

examples of the HO4S-1 for the US Navy in the general-purpose role; and 161 examples of the HRS for the US Marine Corps in the assault transport role, with self-sealing fuel tanks and accommodation for eight troops: the HRS was delivered from April 1951 in two variants as the baseline HRS-1 (60 helicopters) and the HRS-2 (101 helicopters) with improved equipment; a number of HRS-2s were transferred to the UK for use by the FAA under the designation Whirlwind HAR.Mk 21. In the 1962 tri-service rationalisation of the US services' designation systems, surviving examples of the USAF and US Army models became the UH-19A and UH-19C Chickasaw respectively, while the small number of SH-19A and SH-19B helicopters (H-19As and H-19Bs converted to the rescue role) received the revised designations HH-19A and HH-19B respectively.

These S-55A variants had a main rotor with a diameter of 49ft 0in (14.94m). Delivered from 1952, the improved S-55B/C introduced the 700hp (522kW) Wright R-1300-3 radial piston engine, a main rotor with a diameter of 53ft 0in (16.15m), a boom that was angled down by 3.5 degrees to provide better clearance between its upper surface and the rotor blades under extreme circumstances (specifically the S-55C model), a horizontal stabilizer in place of the inverted-Vee finlets, a proper fin in place of the original pylon to carry the tail rotor, and improved equipment. This improved type was built for the USAF as the H-19B (264 helicopters redesignated UH-19B in 1962); for the US Army as the H-19D Chickasaw (301 helicopters redesignated UH-19D Chickasaw in 1962); for the US Navy as the HO4S-3 (79 helicopters redesignated UH-19F in 1962); for the US Coast Guard as the HO4S-3G (30 hoist-equipped helicopters redesignated HH-19G in 1962); and for the US Marine Corps as the HRS-3 (105 helicopters redesignated CH-19E in 1962). A number of HO4S-3s were transferred to the UK for use by the FAA with the designation Whirlwind HAS.Mk 22.

The designation S-55T is now applied to any piston-engined helicopter of the S-55 series revised by Aviation Specialties or Helitec with the 650hp (485kW) Garrett TSE331-3U-303 turboshaft powerplant, whose higher

Opposite: The Mil Mi-4 helicopter, known in the West by the reporting designation 'Hound', was clearly inspired by the Sikorsky S-55 design but was somewhat larger and more powerfully engined than its American counterpart. The type's primary details include a powerplant of one 1,700hp (1,267.5kW) Shvetsov ASh-82V radial piston engine, main rotor diameter of 68ft 11in (21.00m), fuselage length of 53ft 11in (16.435m), height of 13ft 8.25in (4.17m), maximum take-off weight of 17,196lb (7,800kg), maximum speed of 130mph (210km/h) at 4,920ft (1,500m), service ceiling of 18,045ft (5,500m) and range of 155 miles (250km).

An early example of a successful tandem-rotor transport helicopter was the Vertol (originally Piasecki) PV-18 that was ordered by the US Navy as the HUP Retriever and, as seen here, by the US Army as the H-25 that was universally known as the Army Mule. The type was powered by a single 575hp (429kW) Continental R-975-42 radial piston engine driving a transmission system that turned both rotors, and the location of this engine in the rear part of the fuselage is indicated by the use of tailwheel landing gear with the divided main units located well aft on the lower part of the fuselage, as the weight of the air-cooled engine prevented the machine toppling onto its nose.

Seen here in the form of a machine operated by the French navy for the assault transport of marine forces, the Sikorsky S-58 was a larger and considerably more powerful evolution from the concept of the S-55, offering greater payload and performance.

power-to-weight ratio improves payload capability through a major reduction of empty weight, generally enhances performance, and offers the advantages of lower vibration levels.

This American helicopter was one of the world's most successful types ever brought into production, and small numbers are still operational in a variety of civilian and military capacities. Its Soviet counterpart, the Mi-4 that received the NATO reporting designation 'Hound', was a general-purpose machine, and by adapting the main features of the S-55, Mil's design team was able to reduce the time otherwise needed for development.

One year later, Sikorsky responded with the S-56, the world's first twin-engined helicopter, built to a 1950 US Marine Corps requirement for an assault transport helicopter able to carry 26 fully equipped troops or an equivalent weight of freight including light vehicles (three Jeeps) or a 4.13in

Compared with the S-55, the Sikorsky S-58 had a four- rather than three-blade main rotor, a more conventionally configured fuselage with considerable payload volume still accessed by sliding lateral doors, and fixed tailwheel landing gear. The type was operated by the US forces as the H-34 Choctaw (US Army), HSS Seabat (US Navy) and HUS Seahorse (US Marine Corps) and by several other armed services around the world, and was also built under licence in France and the UK, in the latter as the Westland Wessex that reached its definitive form with a turboshaft powerplant.

The Italian company Agusta has produced helicopters of its own design but is best known as the licensee of Bell, Boeing and Sikorsky. This is an Agusta (Bell) AB.47J of the Italian army.

(105mm) howitzer and its crew. Sikorsky designed the S-56 round a hold 30ft 1in (9.17m) long, 7ft 3in (2.21m) wide and 6ft 7in (2.01m) high, accessed by hydraulically powered clamshell doors in the lower nose (as well as by a rear cargo door) and fitted with a winch on an overhead rail for movement of freight items. Of necessity, the hold had to be arranged under the centre of gravity, and this determined the overall layout of the helicopter. The rest of the fuselage comprised a flightdeck above the clamshell nose doors and a comparatively short rear fuselage that supported the upward-angled pylon carrying the four-blade tail rotor. In the absence of turboshaft engines,

In 1962 all the S-58 series helicopters in US service were redesignated in the H-34 series as part of the rationalisation of the three separate systems used up to that time. This is a UH-34D (originally HUS-1 Seahorse) used for the recovery of an astronaut from a Mercury orbiter capsule in the 1960s.

which appeared just a few years later and would have transformed the S-56's capabilities as a result of their smaller size and higher power-to-weight ratio, the required power could only be provided by a pair of large fan-cooled radial piston engines. There was inadequate room in the fuselage for these units, which were thus installed in large nacelles at the tips of stub wings, with their transmission shafts extending inward to the gearbox below the five-blade main rotor. The nacelles also carried the retractable main units of the tailwheel landing gear.

The capabilities promised by the S-56 were good, and the US Marine Corps ordered four XHR2S-1 prototypes with a powerplant of two 1,900hp (1,417kW) R-2800-50 Double Wasp radial piston engines, and the first of these machines flew in December 1953. Successful trials paved the way for the delivery of 55 (out of an initially ordered 91) examples of the HR2S-1 production model with modified engine nacelles, twin-wheel main landing gear units, and a triangular dorsal fillet bracing the tail-rotor pylon to the rear fuselage.

The first HR2S-1 flew in October 1955, and deliveries were completed between July 1956 and February 1959. The designation was changed to CH-37C in the 1962 rationalisation of US designation systems. Impressed by the HR2S's payload capability, the US Navy thought that the type could be developed into a useful radar-equipped airborne early warning (AEW) type, and this resulted in an order for two HR2S-1W helicopters delivered in 1957 with the nose extensively revised with a bulbous radome for the APS-20E

35

surveillance radar, whose consoles and operators were accommodated in the modified hold. Endurance and service ceiling were both poor, however, and no further orders for this AEW version were placed.

The US Army was also interested in the S-56 and, after successful evaluation of one HR2S-1 with the revised designation YH-37, in 1954 ordered the first of an eventual 94 helicopters for service from 1956 with the designation H-37A Mojave that was altered in 1962 to CH-37A Mojave. The initial helicopters were delivered with R-2800-50 engines but later machines had improved R-2800-54 engines, and production was completed in May 1960. In June 1961 the service began to receive 90 helicopters rebuilt to the improved H-37B Mojave (from 1962 CH-37B Mojave) standard with a Lear-developed autostabilization system, a redesigned cargo door and cabin

Generally known in the West by the reporting designation 'Horse', the Yakovlev Yak-24 was designed as a medium transport but was never effective because of continued resonance problems with its tandem-rotor configuration. The details of this type, in its Yak-24U form with a dynamic system that comprised two Mil Mi-4 rotors and associated engines, included a powerplant of two 1,700hp (1,267.5kW) Shvetsov ASh-82V radial piston engines each driving a rotor with a diameter of 68ft 10.75in (21.00m), fuselage length of 69ft 10.5in (21.30m), height of 21ft 4in (6.50m), maximum take-off weight of 32,276lb (14,640kg), maximum speed of 158mph (254km/h) at sea level, service ceiling of 18,045ft (5,500m) and range of 298 miles (480km). The helicopter could carry 40 troops, or 18 litters, or two anti-tank guns with crews and limited ammunition, or two command cars, or three staff cars.

hatch, crash-resistant fuel tanks, the ability to load and unload while hovering, and other operational improvements.

One year after the appearance of the S-56, Sikorsky introduced the S-58 as a general-purpose type that was quickly followed by a specialised anti-submarine version. The S-58 was an outstanding design, and earned very substantial orders from the US armed forces and from other users. The model was also built under licence in the United Kingdom as the Westland Wessex with a turboshaft powerplant of the type later adopted for a number of S-58 conversions. Westland had previously built the S-55 under licence as the Whirlwind, again with a turboshaft powerplant.

The designation S-58A was used for the civil and military general-purpose helicopter that first flew in prototype form during March 1954 as a far more capable machine than the preceding S-55 series, due to the use of a considerably more powerful engine and a replanned fuselage incorporating a larger cabin. The basic S-58 design resulted from a US Navy requirement for an anti-submarine helicopter offering much better capabilities than the HO4S naval version of the S-55, which had been used to a limited extent in the anti-submarine warfare (ASW) role with dunking sonar and an armament or one or two lightweight homing torpedoes, but had revealed wholly inadequate payload/range performance for effective use in this exacting role. The US Navy's hopes for a highly capable shipborne ASW helicopter were based primarily on the Bell Model 61 tandem-rotor type powered by a single 2,400hp (1,789kW) Pratt & Whitney R-2800 Double Wasp radial piston engine, but development was slow and the eventual helicopter was disappointing in performance, and only 50 of these very large HSL-1 helicopters were built.

In the circumstances, therefore, it was fortunate that Sikorsky had begun work during 1951 on the S-58. This was based on an engine offering nearly double the power of that used in the S-55, although this engine was still located in the nose behind clamshell access doors and drove the transmission system by means of a long shaft running obliquely through the forward fuselage to the gearbox under the main rotor. Other changes were four- rather than three-blade main and tail rotors, replacement of the S-55's combination of a pod-and-boom fuselage and quadricycle landing gear by a more conventional fuselage with tailwheel landing gear, and provision for

the main rotor blades and the complete rear fuselage (with tail pylon and anti-torque rotor) to be folded for easier shipborne stowage.

In June 1952 the US Navy ordered three XHSS-1 prototypes, and the first of these flew in March 1954 with a powerplant of one R-1820-84 radial, a crew of two, and provision for 16 passengers or eight litters. The type was ordered into production as the HSS-1 Seabat (from 1962 SH-34G or, stripped of mission equipment for the utility transport role, UH-34G). Despite its greater power, the HSS-1 still lacked the payload/range performance for effective use in the combined submarine hunter and killer roles, however, so the type was generally operated in pairs with one helicopter flying as a submarine hunter with dunking sonar and the other as a submarine killer with one or two lightweight homing torpedoes carried on the fuselage sides. Production totalled 215 helicopters, and this initial model was followed by 167 examples of the HSS-1N (from 1962 SH-34J or, stripped of mission equipment for the utility transport role, UH-34J) night/adverse-weather variant with improved avionics, an autostabilization system, an automatic hover coupling system, and Doppler navigation.

The US Marine Corps adopted the same basic type as the HUS-1 Seahorse (from 1963 UH-34D) of which 516 were delivered with accommodation for 12 fully armed troops and provision for 0.3in (7.62mm) pintle-mounted machine guns in the cabin doors. Other major variants for the USMC were the HUS-1A Seahorse (from 1962 UH-34E) amphibious version of which 40 were delivered with pontoon floats on the three units of the landing gear, and the HUS-1Z Seahorse (from 1962 VH-34D) of which seven were delivered as VIP transports.

The US Army adopted a derivative of the HSS-1 as the H-34A Choctaw (from 1962 CH-34A), and ordered 359 of the type in a utility configuration that was converted in a few cases to VH-34A VIP/staff transport and the upgraded CH-34B and CH-34C standards, the last with airborne search equipment. The CH-34A's hold is 13ft 7in (4.14m) long, 5ft 0in (1.52m)

Developed from the PV-3, the PV-17 first flew in 1949 and was built to the extent of just five Vertol (Piasecki) HRP-2 Rescuer helicopters, used by the US Marine Corps for 10-seat assault transport training with a powerplant of one 600hp (447kW) Pratt & Whitney R-1340-AN-1 Wasp radial piston engine.

The PD-22 design was based on that of the PV-17 with a larger-capacity fuselage and a considerably uprated powerplant, and the type was ordered as the H-21 series for service with the US Air Force and US Army with the names Work Horse and Shawnee respectively. The type reached its definitive form as the Vertol Model 43 (H-21C Shawnee), of which 334 were delivered to the US Army with accommodation for 20 troops or capability for the carriage of freight including a slung load on a ventral lifting hook, powerplant of one 1,425hp (1,062.5kW) Wright R-1820-103 radial piston engine driving two rotors each with a diameter of 44ft 0in (13.41m), fuselage length of 52ft 6in (16.00m), height of 15ft 5in (4.70m), maximum take-off weight of 14,704lb (6,669kg), maximum speed of 125mph (202km/h) at sea level, service ceiling of 7,750ft (2,360m) and range of 403 miles (649km).

wide and 5ft 10in (1.78m) high, and is accessed by a large starboard-side sliding door.

The USAF operated only 10 HH-34D rescue helicopters converted from ex-naval CH-34Ds for the USAF Reserve. Other S-58s were built for civil use and for export to the air arms of allied nations, raising Sikorsky production to 1,821 helicopters. Another 166 helicopters were built under licence in France by Sud-Aviation with no major divergence from the US basic pattern, and a somewhat different version was built in the UK as the Westland Wessex. The type is still in limited service, and most survivors conform in general terms to the standard described above. The designation S-58T is used for S-58s revised with a turbine powerplant, namely one 1,875hp (1,398kW) Pratt & Whitney Canada PT6B-6 Turbo Twin Pac coupled turboshaft. The revised powerplant results in improved reliability and payload, the latter deriving from the turboshaft's considerably better power-to-weight ratio. Sikorsky flew the first such conversion in August 1970, and a similar package is available in the early 1990s from California Helicopter International.

Enter the Turboshaft

The Sikorsky HH-53 Super Jolly was developed from the CH-53 Sea Stallion for the combat search-and-rescue role with a rescue hoist, armour protection, armament, all-weather flight and navigation instrumentation, and additional fuel capacity that could be supplemented in flight via a retractable refuelling probe on the lower starboard side of the forward fuselage.

MOST of the helicopters built up to the mid-1950s, in any part of the world, had a cruising speed of just under 100mph (160km/h) and a range in the order of 250 miles (400km). The main differentiating factor in their performance, therefore, had been the load they could carry. This increased rapidly in later types, and in the next generation of helicopters the performance also improved.

The reason for this improvement was a combination of two factors, one of them relatively simple and the other considerably more important. The simple factor was the general improvement in the helicopter concept during this period, witnessed by the adoption of improved structures and the introduction of more sophisticated aerodynamic and control features. The more important factor, however, was the replacement of the air-cooled radial or opposed piston engine by the turboshaft. The major advantages offered by the turboshaft over the piston engine were its comparatively vibration-free running (as the core of the engine consisted of rotating rather than reciprocating parts), its much improved reliability, its greater economy of fuel, and its radically reduced size and weight. This last advantage allowed the engine or engines to be installed above the cabin close to the rotor mast rather than in the lower fuselage, at a stroke removing the need for long and weighty transmission shafts and removing a bulky item whose volume could now be used for payload. The overall effect of the change from a reciprocating to a turbine engine was therefore a powerplant offering not only higher power in absolute terms but also a significantly higher power-to-weight ratio.

An indication of general improvement came in 1955 with the performance of the turboshaft-powered Alouette II: cruising speed rose to nearly 115mph (185km/h) and range to 400 miles (645km), and the model sold widely to civil and military operators in many parts of the world. The Alouette was the world's first turboshaft-powered helicopter to enter full production, and its origins can be traced back to the Sud-Est SE.3120 Alouette three-seat helicopter designed largely for agricultural use. This first flew in July 1952 with a powerplant of one 200hp (149kW) Salmson 9NH radial piston engine. The airframe was then completely revised to accept a turboshaft powerplant, the 360hp (269kW) Turbomeca Artouste I, and this SE.3130 prototype first took to the air in March 1955, being followed in 1956 by three pre-production helicopters.

The type entered production in 1956 as a utility helicopter for the civil as

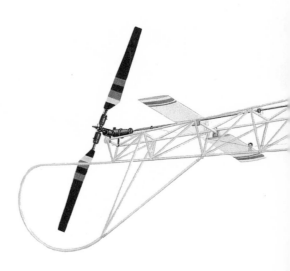

well as military markets, but when Sud-Est merged with Sud-Aviation in 1957, the designation was altered to SE.313B. The Sud-Aviation and Nord-Aviation organisations merged in January 1970 to create Aérospatiale, and it is as a product of this manufacturer that the Alouette series is generally known despite the fact that surviving helicopters really come under the aegis of Eurocopter France, as Aérospatiale became upon its merger with the German company MBB (that became Eurocopter Deutschland).

The Alouette II soon proved itself a very capable general-purpose helicopter, being distinguished particularly for its excellent capabilities at higher altitudes, and at its peak served with some 22 air arms. Production amounted to 923 helicopters for civil and military operators. Apart from what was for the time good performance, the Alouette II was notable for its ability to carry a slung load of 1,323lb (600kg). The type is now obsolete except in the communications role but is still in fairly widespread service with a powerplant of one Turbomeca Artouste IIC6 turboshaft derated from 530 to 360shp (395 to 269kW).

The SE.3140 Alouette II, a development of the SE.3130 powered by one 400hp (298kW) Turbomeca Turmo II turboshaft, did not enter production, so the next model was the SA.318C Alouette II Astazou. First flown in January 1961, this is a much-improved version of the SE.313B, with the more fuel-efficient Astazou IIA turboshaft derated for greater reliability in this application. Production lasted into 1975, some 350 helicopters being built, and of the Alouette II series some 963 went to military operators, many of these machines remaining in service as utility helicopters.

The year in which the Alouette II first flew also saw the introduction of the first variants of the world's only truly successful co-axial twin-rotor helicopter series, namely the Kamov Ka-15 'Hen' and Ka-18 'Hog'. These entered service with the Soviet army and navy, and were also used by Aeroflot, the Soviet airline organisation. The performance of these two

Kamov helicopters was inferior to that of the Alouette II, but their importance lies in the fact that they paved the way for the Ka-25 'Hormone'.

Further development of the Alouette II concept resulted in the more capable, better known, more widely produced and still useful SA.316A Alouette III. Designed as the SE.3160 in the period after the 1957 merger between Sud-Est and Sud-Aviation, the Alouette III was a basic upgrading and updating of the Alouette II, and featured greater power, a fully covered pod-and-boom fuselage, a larger cabin, improved equipment and other enhancements to offer greater payload and better performance together with the reliability and altitude performance of the Alouette II. The prototype first flew in February 1959, and production followed in 1961 with a powerplant of one 870hp (649kW) Turbomeca Artouste IIB turboshaft derated to 570hp (425kW) and matched to an upgraded transmission system. The type soon revealed exceptional high-altitude performance even with a substantial load, and this was a great spur to military as well as civil sales.

The SA.316B Alouette III improved model was introduced in 1968 with the uprated powerplant of one Artouste IIIB turboshaft, a strengthened transmission and improved landing gear for a further increase in payload. The type was also built under licence in Switzerland by FFA. The SA.316C Alouette III was a limited-production version powered by the Artouste IIID turboshaft, but the definitive model was the SA.319B Alouette III Astazou. Just as the SA.318C was developed as an Astazou-powered SE.313B, the SA.319B was produced and first flown in 1967 as a more economical and reliable machine than the SA.316B. Production of the Alouette III series

Left and below: The Aérospatiale (now Eurocopter France) SA. 318 Alouette II series was the first turboshaft-powered helicopter in the world to enter large-scale production, and its overall superiority to piston-engined light helicopters was rewarded by large orders. In its definitive SA. 318C Alouette II Astazou form, this helicopter can carry its pilot and up to four passengers, and its other details include a powerplant of one 530hp (395kW) Turbomeca Astazou IIA turboshaft derated to 360hp (268kW), a main rotor diameter of 33ft 5.6in (10.20m), fuselage length of 31ft 11.75in (9.75m), height of 9ft 0.25in (2.75m), maximum take-off weight of 3,630lb (1,650kg), maximum speed of 127mph (205km/h) at sea level, service ceiling of 10,825ft (3,300m) and range of 62 miles (100km) with a 1,323lb (600kg) payload.

began only in 1973 and amounted to 1,453 helicopters, the greater portion of them for military service in a number of roles. The HAL Chetak is the Indian licence-built version of the SA.316B, which HAL has developed into role-optimised land and naval subvariants. The land version is designed for the anti-tank role with four air-to-surface missiles (ASMs) and a stabilized roof sight, while the naval version is intended for the shipborne anti-submarine role and is armed with two Mk 44 or Mk 46 anti-submarine torpedoes (only one torpedo is carried if the optional podded magnetic-anomoly detection (MAD) kit is fitted), a harpoon-type downhaul system for ship capability under adverse weather and sea conditions, and folding rotor blades for economical shipboard stowage. The last basic development of the Alouette series was the SA.315B Lama, which was evolved from a time late in 1968 by Sud-Aviation to meet an Indian requirement for a general-purpose helicopter with good hot-and-high performance for Himalayan operations. The SA.315B first flew in March 1969, and is the airframe of the Alouette II combined with the dynamic system of the Alouette III. The type entered service in 1970, and the versions built under licence in India and Brazil are the HAL Cheetah (built from 1972 and still in low-volume production in the mid-1990s) and the Helibras HB 315B Gaviao.

The most important helicopter adopted by the US forces up to that time appeared in 1956. This was the Bell Model 204, which was the US forces' first turbine-powered helicopter and was designed as a nine-seat utility type that entered service as the HU-1 (later UH-1) Iroquois but is best remembered as the 'Huey' of the Vietnam War. In the basic model, the continued improvement in helicopter performance was indicated by a cruising speed of 126mph (205km/h) combined with a range of 320 miles (515km). The Model 204 variants were powered by variants of the Lycoming T53 turboshaft rated at between 770 and 1,100hp (574 and 820kW), and these were followed by larger numbers of the Model 205 variants with accommodation for 15 men including the pilot, and an uprated T53 powerplant rated at between 1,100 and 1,400hp (820 and 1,044kW). Variants of these two basic types were converted and developed into a host of special combat roles, the most significant of which was the Model 209 HueyCobra

The piston-engined helicopter was not immediately replaced by the turboshaft-powered type once the turboshaft had emerged as an effective powerplant in the mid-1950s, and helicopters such as this Kaman H-43A Huskie, with a powerplant of one 600hp (447kW) Pratt & Whitney R-1340-43 radial piston engine, lingered in its primary task of base rescue with the US Air Force. The type was then transformed by the adoption of a turboshaft powerplant, the 860hp (641kW) Lycoming T53-L-1B, to create the H-43B.

The Aérospatiale (now Eurocopter France) Alouette III was developed as an enlarged and more powerful version of the Alouette II, with an uprated engine, a higher-rated transmission and an enclosed tailboom. The original model was the SA. 316C Alouette III with accommodation for the pilot and up to six passengers, or two litters and two attendants, or 1,653lb (750kg) of freight, a powerplant of one 870hp (649kW) Turbomeca Artouste III turboshaft derated to 570hp (425kW), main rotor diameter of 36ft 1.75in (11.02m), fuselage length of 33ft 4.375in (10.17m), height of 9ft 10.125in (3.00m), maximum take-off weight of 4,960lb (2,250kg), maximum speed of 136mph (220km/h) at sea level, service ceiling of 13,125ft (4,000m) and range of 298 miles (400km). Like the Alouette II series, the Alouette III was produced in Artouste and higher-rated Astazou-powered forms that sold well on both the civil and military markets, and was also developed in specialised forms with armament and the appropriate sensors.

armed combat helicopter. This was evolved for the close support of the troops landed from 'Huey' helicopters, and was in essence a narrow-fuselage derivative of the Model 204 with the dynamic system of the Model 205. Setting a pattern that has remained essentially unaltered in the intervening years, the fuselage accommodated the pilot above and behind the co-pilot/gunner: the pilot could fire the disposable armament carried on the four hardpoints under the HueyCobra's stub wings, but the primary weapon operator was the co-pilot/gunner who also handled the chin-mounted traversing turret with its elevating armament of one multi-barrel machine gun and one grenade launcher. Quickly evolved and simply equipped, the HueyCobra was then evolved into more powerful variants with heavier and more versatile armament aimed with the aid of increasingly sophisticated avionics.

The HueyCobra is still in widespread service in its latest AH-1S form (four subvariants). A two-engined version was developed for use by the US Marine Corps, and the original AH-1J SeaCobra has since been replaced by the upgraded AH-1T Improved SeaCobra and the AH-1W SuperCobra. All these Model 204, Model 205 and Model 209 variants retain the two-blade type of main rotor introduced on the original HU-1, but Bell is continuing development of the narrow-fuselage marque and offers a much enhanced model with a four-blade main rotor.

The origins of the 'Huey' series can be traced back to the Korean War, which revealed the importance of the helicopter for a number of utility roles including, most importantly of all, casualty evacuation. A study undertaken after the war by Bell indicated that much improved operational capability could only be achieved in a helicopter that was both larger and more powerful than those currently in service, and in 1954 the US Army issued a

requirement for a utility helicopter able to carry a payload of 800lb (363kg) over a radius of 115 miles (1,85km), fly at a speed of 115mph (185km/h), hover at 6,000ft (1,830m) out of ground effect, and be air-portable in transports such as the Douglas C-124 Globemaster and Lockheed C-130 Hercules.

The requirement elicited 20 design proposals, and in June 1955 the US Army announced that the winner of the design competition was Bell with its Model 204 concept that was initially ordered in the form of three XH-40 prototypes. The core of the new helicopter was the new Lycoming T53 turboshaft, a basically simple and conservative engine that offered early maturity and considerable growth potential from its initial rating of 700hp (522kW). In overall terms, the advantages that the US Army found in the turboshaft by comparison with the piston engine were less vibration, reduced mechanical complexity, smaller volume, lower weight, much improved power-to-weight ratio, reduced fire risk, and the ability to run on a wide range of fuels.

With this turboshaft as the heart of its design, Bell based the all-metal Model 204 on a tadpole-shaped fuselage with a broad forward section accommodating the flightdeck area (accessed by two hinged doors) forward of the payload area (accessed by two large sliding doors), twin-skid landing gear, and the turboshaft located above the fuselage at the junction of the tail boom with the main pod section. The gearbox was installed in front of the engine and drove a two-blade main rotor (of the standard Bell type with broad blades and a stabilizing bar located at right angles to the blades) and a two-blade anti-torque rotor located on the port side of the pylon that was placed well behind the tailplane on the tail boom.

The Sikorsky CH-3C was developed as a purely land-based derivative of the SH-3 Sea King with its boat hull and stabilizing floats, and proved very useful in the utility transport role.

The Westland Wessex was a British-developed version of the Sikorsky S-58 with a turboshaft powerplant that initially comprised a 1,450hp (1,081kW) Napier Gazelle Mk 161 but later two 1,250hp (932kW) Rolls-Royce Gnome Mk 112 (licence-built General Electric T58) turboshafts. This is a Wessex HU.Mk 5 assault transport with details that included a rotor diameter of 56ft 0in (17.07m), fuselage length of 48ft 4.5in (14.74m), height of 14ft 5in (4.39m), maximum take-off weight of 13,500lb (6,124kg), maximum speed of 132mph (212km/h) at sea level, service ceiling of 14,100ft (4,295m) and range of 478 miles (770km).

The first XH-40 flew in October 1956 with a powerplant of one 700hp (522kW) XT53-L-1 turboshaft, and by this time the US Army had also ordered six YH-40 service test helicopters with a powerplant of one 700hp (522kW) T53-L-1A turboshaft, the cabin lengthened by 1ft 0in (0.305m) to allow the carriage of four litters, greater ground clearance, and improved controls. The two types were later redesignated XHU-1 and YHU-1, as the pre-production model was to be the first type in the US Army's new HU (Helicopter Utility) category. The pre-production model, of which just nine were delivered from June 1959 with the 860hp (641kW) T53-L-1A turboshaft flat-rated at 770hp (574kW), was the HU-1 Iroquois (redesignated UH-1 in the 1962 rationalisation).

After the HU-1 had entered production for the US Army, Bell evolved a civil version as the Model 204B with a powerplant of one 1,100hp (820kW) Lycoming T53-L-1A turboshaft for the carriage of 10 passengers, and some of these helicopters entered limited military service with export customers. After the delivery of the nine HU-1 (UH-1) pre-production helicopters, full-production helicopters entered service from June 1959 with the designation HU-1A (later UH-1A). With a powerplant of one T53-L-1A turboshaft driving a main rotor on a shorter mast, the type accommodated a crew of one or two plus up to five passengers or two litters, or alternatively 3,000lb (1,361kg) of freight in a cabin that was 8ft 6in (2.59m) long, 7ft 10in (2.39m) wide and 4ft 10in (1.47m) high. Later helicopters of the same basic variant switched to the 960hp (716kW) T53-L-5 turboshaft for improved performance with the same load, and the type could be armed with two 0.3in (7.62mm) pintle-mounted machine guns and thirty-two 2.75in (70mm) unguided rockets in two packs on the fuselage sides. Production up to March 1961 amounted to 173 helicopters, of which 14 were converted into TH-1A Iroquois dual-control trainers.

Introduced to service in March 1961, the HU-1B (soon UH-1B) was an updated version with a powerplant of one 960hp (716kW) T53-L-5 turboshaft or, in later examples of the same basic variant, one 1,100hp (820kW) T53-L-9/9A or T53-L-11 turboshaft driving a main rotor with wider-chord blades and located on top of a taller rotor mast. The type can carry seven troops, or three litters and two seated casualties plus one attendant, or 3,000lb (1,361kg) of freight, and can be fitted with the same armament installations as the UH-1A. Production between 1961 and 1965 totalled 1,014 helicopters including the four service test helicopters.

The UH-1C model, introduced to service in September 1965, is based closely on the UH-1B but with a longer fuselage, increased fuel capacity, a main rotor with blades of even wider chord for a modest improvement in speed, and much greater manoeuvrability as a result of a reduced main rotor blade stall tendency. Production amounted to 749 helicopters.

Entering service from February 1964, the UH-1E was the UH-1B/C variant designed to fulfil the US Marine Corps' assault support helicopter (ASH) requirement, with an all-aluminium structure to mitigate the effects of salt-water corrosion, a rotor brake, increased fuel capacity, a rescue winch, and a payload of eight troops or 4,000lb (1,814kg) of freight. Production between 1964 and 1966 amounted to 192 helicopters, and there were also 20 examples of the TH-1E crew trainer variant.

The UH-1F that entered service from September 1964 was the UH-1B utility version for the USAF, with a completely different powerplant in the form of one 1,290hp (962kW) General Electric T58-GE-3 turboshaft flat-rated at 1,100hp (820kW) for the carriage of a payload comprising 10 passengers or 4,000lb (1,814kg) of freight in the missile site-support role. Production between September 1964 and 1967 amounted to 119 helicopters excluding 26 examples of the TH-1F dual-control trainer variant.

The HH-1K was the SAR variant of the UH-1E for the US Navy, but powered by the 1,400hp (1,044kW) T53-L-13 turboshaft. Production amounted to 27 helicopters delivered from May 1970. The UH-1L was the utility variant of the UH-1E for the US Navy, but powered by the T53-L-13 turboshaft derated to 1,100hp (820kW). Production amounted to eight helicopters delivered from November 1968, and there were also 90 examples of the TH-1L dual-control trainer delivered from 1969. The UH-1M designation was applied to a small number of UH-1Cs upgraded with the T53-L-13 turboshaft, provision for six AGM-22A (French AS.11) wire-guided anti-tank missiles and, in some helicopters, the Hughes Iroquois night fighter and night tracker (INFANT) system of searchlights and a low-light-level TV to illuminate targets for the side-firing armament. The UH-1P designation was applied to 20 UH-1Fs converted for psychological warfare.

The Model 204 series was also built under licence in Italy and Japan. In Italy the type was known as the Agusta (Bell) AB 204B, and its construction was a logical development from Agusta's production of the Bell Model 47 light helicopter as the Agusta (Bell) AB 47. This was powered as standard by the Lycoming T53-L-11A turboshaft, but alternative engines were the General Electric T58-GE-3 and Bristol Siddeley (later Rolls-Royce) Gnome

Designed as the Model 204, the Bell UH-1 Iroquois, universally nicknamed 'Huey' after its initial pre-1962 HU-1 designation, was the first turboshaft-powered helicopter to enter large-scale production in the USA and was one of the weapons that may be said to have defined the nature of the Vietnam War, in which American forces were involved between 1961 and 1973. The UH-1B may be taken as typical of the early 'Huey' helicopters, and could carry the pilot and up to eight soldiers, or two litters and one attendant, or 3,000lb (1,361kg) of freight. Other details included a powerplant of one 96hp (716kW) Lycoming T53-L-5 turboshaft, main rotor diameter of 44ft 0in (13.41m), fuselage length of 42ft 7in (12.98m), height of 12ft 8.5in (3.87m), maximum take-off weight of 8,500lb (3,856kg), maximum speed of 138mph (222km/h) at sea level, service ceiling of 14,000ft (4,265m) and range of 230 miles (371km).

H.1000 or H.1200 turboshafts. The first AB 204B flew in May 1961, and the four main subvariants of the baseline utility helicopter were the AB 204B-11 with the H.1000 engine and a main rotor diameter of 44ft 0in (13.41m), the AB 204B-12 with the H.1000 engine and a main rotor diameter of 48ft 0in (14.63m), the AB 204B-21 with the H.1200 engine and the smaller-diameter main rotor, and the AB 204B-22 with the H.1200 engine and the larger-diameter main rotor.

The most important development, however, was the AB 204AS dedicated anti-submarine helicopter: this was powered by the T58-GE-3 turboshaft, its armament comprised two Mk 44 or Mk 46 lightweight homing torpedoes, and its mission equipment included dunking sonar, all-weather instrumentation, automatic stabilisation and approach to the hover, and optional search radar. Production of the AB 204 series continued to 1974 and totalled 238 helicopters.

In January 1962, Bell granted a licence for the Model 204 to Mitsui, which in turn sub-licensed the type to Fuji for manufacture as the Fuji (Bell) UH-1B with the tail rotor relocated from the port to the starboard side of the tail pylon and with power provided by the T53 turboshaft assembled in Japan as the Kawasaki KT53. Deliveries totalled 124 helicopters, all but 34 of these going to the Japanese Ground Self-Defense Force.

Service experience revealed that the Model 204, in its UH-1 military form, was limited in tactical utility by its comparatively small payload volume and indifferent performance under hot-and-high conditions, both of these being factors that were to come to the fore in operations over South Vietnam during the Vietnam War (American involvement between 1961 and 1973). Bell therefore decided to exploit the greater power available from the T53-L-11 engine in the development of a Model 204 derivative with a larger main rotor and a bigger cabin for the carriage of a considerably greater payload: not counting its one pilot, this could include 12 troops, or six litters plus one attendant, or 4,000lb (1,814kg) of freight.

The new type was designed as the Model 205, and in July 1960 the US Army ordered seven examples with the service test designation YUH-1D. The first of these helicopters flew in August 1961 with a powerplant of one 1,100hp (820kW) Lycoming T53-L-11 turboshaft, a main rotor with a diameter of 48ft 0in (14.63m) rather than 44ft 0in (13.41m), and a fuselage stretched by 3ft 5in

The Agusta (Bell) AB 204B was the version of the civil Bell Model 204B made in Italy for military as well as civil applications. A notable feature is the typical Bell main rotor design, with two wide-chord blades and, at right angles to them, the stabilizing bar with small weights at its tips.

Operational experience revealed that the UH-1 'Huey' was too small, in its original Model 204 variants, for genuinely effective practical use, so Bell developed the Model 205 with a revised fuselage allowing the incorporation of a cabin large enough to carry up to 14 troops, or six litters and an attendant, or 3,880lb (1,759kg) of freight. The type entered service as the UH-1D, and this is the AB 205 variant built in Italy by Agusta, one of Bell's European licensees. The details for the definitive UH-1H variant include a powerplant of one 1,400hp (1,044kW) Lycoming T53-L-13 turboshaft, main rotor diameter of 48ft 0in (14.63m), fuselage length of 41ft 10.75in (12.77m), height of 14ft 6in (4.42m), maximum take-off weight of 9,500lb (4,309kg), maximum speed of 127mph (204km/h) at 5,700ft (1,735m), service ceiling of 12,600ft (3,840m) and range of 320 miles (515km).

(1.04m). In concert with a relocation of the enlarged fuel cells, the fuselage stretch increased cabin volume by slightly more than 50 per cent and made possible the carriage of the planned maximum payload in any of its forms.

The Model 205 was intended mainly for the US military, but Bell appreciated that the type also had civil attractions and therefore introduced the Model 205A-1 upgraded version that also secured a number of export military sales. First flown in 1963, the type is powered by a 1,400hp (1,044kW) Lycoming T53-13-B turboshaft derated to 1,250hp (932kW) and can carry a slung load of 5,000lb (2,268kg) as an alternative to an internal payload of 14 passengers.

The initial production version of the Model 205 for the US Army entered service from August 1963 as the UH-1D with a powerplant of one 1,100hp (820kW) T53-L-11 turboshaft, and production amounted to 2,008 helicopters excluding the seven YUH-1D service test helicopters. Profiting from its experience with the Model 205A-1 and its T53-13-B turboshaft, Bell developed an improved version of the UH-1D as the UH-1H with a more powerful engine for better hot-and-high performance, especially in the hover in regions such as South Vietnam. The type was delivered from September 1967, and American production amounted to 4,890 helicopters including 3,573 for the US Army, which plans to maintain some 2,700 helicopters of this type in service into the next century with updated features such as composite main rotor blades (glassfibre and Nomex with polyurethane leading edges protected over their outer sections by a stainless steel capping), an infra-red (IR)suppressor, a crash-resistant auxiliary fuel system, and more modern electronics including a radar-warning receiver and IR jammer, improved radio gear, and possibly a more modern powerplant offering marginally greater power but, more importantly, reduced fuel consumption and better 'maintainability'.

Among the American fleet are several special-purpose models, the most important being the EH-1H. During the early 1980s a few UH-1Hs were converted to the battlefield electronic countermeasures (ECM) standard with the 'Quick Fix I' communications interception, direction-finding and jamming equipment together with the Racal RACJAM airborne communications jamming system. The increasing threat to battlefield helicopters during this period was reflected by other changes such as the addition of a radar-warning receiver, radar jammer, chaff/flare dispenser, IR jammer, and missile detection and countermeasures implementation system. Another battlefield development of the UH-1H was the UH-1H stand-off target acquisition system (SOTAS) targeting helicopter fitted with a General Dynamics radar (with moving target indication facility) using a ventral antenna.

Some 220 UH-1Hs were also converted into UH-1V casevac/medevac helicopters during the 1980s. The designation HH-1H is applied to 30 USAF on-base rescue helicopters based on the UH-1H but carrying special equipment for rescue of aircrew from crashed aircraft.

The Agusta (Bell) AB 205 is the Italian licence-built version of the UH-1D/H differing only in small details from the US pattern, and from 1969 the company produced the slightly improved AB 205A-1. Production ended in 1988 after the delivery of 490 helicopters, mostly to air arms. The AIDC (Bell) UH-1H is the Taiwanese-built version of the UH-1H, of which 118 were delivered by the Aero Industry Development Center between 1969 and 1976. The Dornier (Bell) UH-1D is the German-built version of the UH-1D: after assembling an initial four helicopters from Bell-supplied kits, Dornier produced 140 UH-1Ds for the West German air force (which also received two such helicopters directly from Bell), and another 204 for the West German army. The Fuji (Bell) HU-1H is a version of the UH-1H built under licence by Fuji under sub-licence from Mitsui with the 1,400hp (1,044kW) Kawasaki (Lycoming) T53-K-13B turboshaft with a tractor rather than pusher tail rotor. The first HU-1H flew in July 1973, and military production totalled 107 including 52 with the ability to carry mine dispensers.

The Bell Model 206 was designed in an effort to win a US Army order for a light observation helicopter, but initially lost to the Hughes Model 369 that was ordered as the OH-6 Cayuse, was then developed into the Model 206A for civil sales and finally ordered into large-scale production for the US Army as the OH-58 Kiowa after the Kiowa's delivery rate decreased and its price rose. This is an AB 206 built by Agusta for the Italian army's air corps. The details of the Model 206A include accommodation for the pilot and three passengers or light freight, powerplant of one 317hp (236kW) Allison 250-C18 turboshaft, main rotor diameter of 33ft 4in (10.16m), fuselage length of 31ft 2in (9.50m), height of 9ft 6.5in (2.91m), maximum take-off weight of 3,000lb (1,361kg), maximum speed of 150mph (241km/h) at sea level, service ceiling of 17,000ft (5,180m) and range of 391 miles (629km).

During the early 1960s Bell decided that the only practical way in which its in-service Model 205 (UH-1 Iroquois) utility helicopter could be improved in overall capabilities was through the adoption of an uprated powerplant. There were no single-turboshaft powerplants offering adequate output, however, so the company's thoughts turned to a twin-engined layout. In 1964, Bell converted a UH-1D helicopter to Model 208 Twin Delta configuration with a Continental XT67-T-1 coupled turboshaft: offering 1,240hp (925kW), this powerplant comprised two T72-T-2 Model 217 power units driving a single shaft via a combining gearbox. The Model 208 first flew in April 1965 and offered some performance and payload enhancements over the basic UH-1C, but also the far greater safety factor of a powerplant either of whose power sections could support the helicopter in level flight. It was this latter factor that appealed to the Canadian forces, which needed a twin-engined UH-1 version for the extra reliability and safety required for operations in remote areas. In May 1968, therefore, Canada contracted for the development of the Model 212 Twin Two-Twelve as a derivative of the UH-1H with a Canadian coupled-turboshaft powerplant.

The first Model 212 flew in April 1969 with the 1,290hp (1,150kW) Pratt & Whitney Canada PT6T-3 Turbo Twin Pac driving a semi-rigid rotor of two-blade configuration. Later production models feature the PT6T-3B version of the Turbo Twin Pac with improved single-engine performance. The Model 212 received civil certification in June 1971, and since that time significant numbers of the basic commercial version have been built for the civil market and for the export military market. In October 1983, Textron agreed with the Canadian government to switch production of its current generation of unarmed helicopters to Canada, and the transfer of Model 212 production was completed in August 1988. The Canadian company handles sales to the Canadian government and civil operators, but also supplies helicopters to the parent company for resale to American and other customers. The Model 212 is also built under license in Italy as the Agusta (Bell) AB 212 by Agusta, which has also developed the specialised AB 212ASV/ASW version for the maritime role.

The Bell OH-58 Kiowa was developed during the 1980s into the altogether more capable OH-58D Kiowa Warrior (company designation Model 406) to serve as an advanced scout and target-designation helicopter with an uprated powerplant, refined nose contours, a four-blade main rotor offering greater lift and reduced noise, provision for light armament and, most importantly of all, a mast-mounted sight located above the main rotor. The availability of this multi-sensor item allows the OH-58D to lurk behind cover such as trees or hilltops, where it is relatively immune to the enemy's weapons, but still see the target area with the sensors in the spherical head, which is all that protrudes above the skyline.

Seen here with the wings that can be fitted to offload the six-blade main rotor in forward flight, the Mil Mi-6 'Hook' is an elderly type that still offers considerable heavy-lift capabilities as, with a crew of five, it can carry 90 troops, or 41 litters and two attendants, or 26,455lb (12,000kg) of freight in the hold, or alternatively a slung load of 17,637lb (8,000kg). The type has a powerplant of two 5,499hp (4,100kW) Soloviev D-25V (TV-2BM) turboshafts, rotor diameter of 114ft 10in (35.00m), fuselage length of 108ft 10.5in (33.18m), height of 32ft 4in (9.86m), maximum take-off weight of 93,700lb (42,500kg), maximum speed of 186mph (300km/h) at optimum altitude, service ceiling of 14,765ft (4,500m) and range of 621 miles (1,000km) with a 17,637lb (8,000kg) payload.

Transport Helicopters

HELICOPTERS optimised for the heavy transport role can take one of two primary forms, especially in the USSR (now CIS) that was and remains the primary exponent of such helicopters for civil as well as military purposes. The more obvious of these configurations, as epitomised by the Mil Mi-6 'Hook' and considerably larger and more modern Mi-26 'Halo', is the large fuselage. The floor and lower sides of such a fuselage are generally completed with specialised attachments that allow the insertion of a large number of seats for the passenger-carrying role or, in the more common military role, provide for the firm lashing of freight items. The cabin is generally of rectangular section to maximise the amount of freight that can be loaded onto the strengthened floor, and the capability for straight-in loading and unloading of such freight is provided by the incorporation of rear doors of either the clamshell type with a detachable ramp or, more usually, the rear ramp/door type built into the lower part of the rear fuselage. Such ramp/doors are also a feature of the larger types of American medium transport helicopter such as the Boeing H-46 Sea Knight and H-47 Chinook and also the Sikorsky H-53 Sea Stallion and Super Stallion. The other type of heavy-lift helicopter is the flying crane, which is optimised for the lifting role with a vestigial fuselage reinforced for the attachment of a substantial slung load. Helicopters of this type include the Soviet Mil Mi-10 'Harke' and American Sikorsky H-54 Tarhe. These helicopters generally have tall, wide-straddling quadricycle landing gear of the type that allows the helicopter to taxi over a large load for the attachment of the lifting strop, but the nature of this landing gear also makes it possible to attach a payload pod to the underside of the fuselage or alternatively a payload platform to the inner sides of the landing gear legs.

The Model 212 was adopted by the US military with the designation UH-1N, and deliveries were made from 1970 to the USAF (79 helicopters), and more importantly from 1971 to the US Navy and Marine Corps (221 helicopters of which the last was handed over in 1978). The variant's cabin is 7ft 8in (2.34m) long excluding the cockpit, 8ft 0in (2.44m) wide and 4ft 1in (1.24m) high, and is accessed on each side by a large rearward-sliding door. The sole derivative of this baseline model is the VN-1N presidential and VIP transport helicopter. Production amounted to just two new-build helicopters, although six more were produced as UH-1N conversions.

The Model 412 is a useful helicopter developed as an upgraded version of the Model 212 with a four- rather than two-blade main rotor and greater fuel capacity to increase speed and range. The type first flew in August 1979, and immediately revealed not only better performance but also reduced noise and vibration levels with its powerplant of one 1,800hp (1,342kW) Pratt & Whitney Canada PT6T-3B-1 Turbo Twin Pac coupled turboshaft flat-rated at 1,308hp (975kW) for take-off and 1,130hp (843kW) for continuous running. The type was designed primarily for the civil market, but a number of military orders were also won. The type is also built under licence in Italy as the Agusta (Bell) AB 412.

The Military 412 is the attack transport derivative of the Model 412, and was originally designated Model 412AH. The type has a Lucas undernose

turret (fitted with one 0.5in/12.7mm Browning M3 heavy machine gun and 875 rounds) aimed via a Honeywell Head Tracker helmet sight, provision for 0.3in (7.62mm) machine guns pintle-mounted in the cabin doors, and capability for externally carried weapons such as two pods carrying either two 0.3in machine guns or one 0.5in heavy machine gun, or two pods each carrying one 20mm cannon, or two multiple launchers each carrying seven or nineteen 2.75in (70mm) unguided rockets, or two multiple launchers each carrying four 2.75in unguided rockets. Other variants of the Model 412 include the Model 412SP upgraded version of the Model 412 with an increased maximum take-off weight and some 55 per cent more internal fuel capacity, the Model 412HP 1991 model with improved transmission for a higher hovering ceiling despite the type's greater weight, and the IPTN Bell-412 Indonesian license-built version of the Model 412SP without any significant differences from the baseline version.

As the Western world was concentrating its design and production efforts on the creation of light and medium helicopters for the battlefield role, the USSR was concentrating more on the development of medium and heavy helicopters for tactical and battlefield use. The first of these was the Soviet Mil Mi-6 'Hook', which brought a new dimension to heavy-lift helicopter capabilities, setting world records with payloads of more than 44,092lb (20,000kg). First flown in September 1957, the Mi-6 'Hook-A' was for its time the world's largest helicopter and is still a prodigious machine powered by two 5,499hp (4,100kW) PNPP 'Aviadvigatel' (Soloviev) D-25V (TV-2BM) turboshafts and capable of lifting a substantial slung load as an alternative to the internal payload of troops, freight and light vehicles in the hold, which is accessed by clamshell rear doors and ramps, and is 38ft 6in (11.72m) long, 8ft 8.25in (2.65m) wide and a minimum of 6ft 6in (2.00m) high, with a winch available for cargo handling. An unusual feature of the design is the removable wing, which offloads the main rotor by some 20 per cent in forward flight. Production totalled more than 800 such helicopters, about half of them for dedicated military service and the remainder mainly for the resources-exploitation industry with reversion to military service in times of crisis.

Produced only in small numbers, the Mi-6VKP 'Hook-B' is the airborne command post variant with the cabin fitted out for its role with specialised communication and plotting equipment. The type is distinguishable by its different antennae, which include four blade antennae arranged around the rear of the boom and a large rectangular frame antenna farther forward under the boom. Other changes include the omission of the starboard-side external fuel tank and the installation farther forward on the port side of the fuselage of a heat exchanger associated with the helicopter's additional electronics. The Mi-6AYa 'Hook-C', otherwise known as the Mi-22, is a modernised airborne command post variant with a different electronic suite to that of the 'Hook-B'. The variant is readily identifiable by the large swept blade antenna above the boom, and by the cluster of antennae under the forward fuselage.

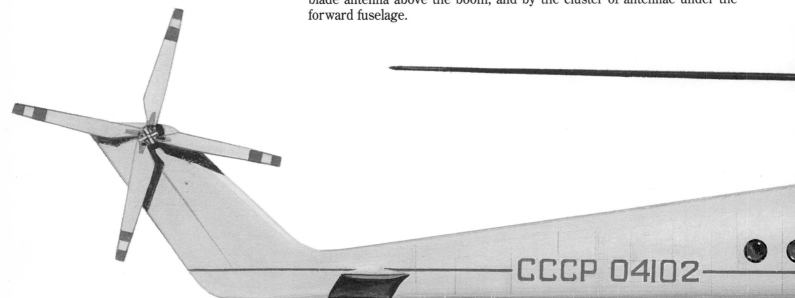

CCCP 04102

The Mi-10 'Harke' is the flying crane half-brother of the Mi-6 'Hook' with a cut-down fuselage and revised landing gear. The type is seen here with the platform that can be installed inside the landing gear units for the carriage of items such as this wheeled armoured personnel carrier. This and other heavy-lift helicopters have been produced in modest numbers for dual civil and military use: in civil service, the helicopters operate in tasks such as the supply of resources-exploitation industries in Siberia and similarly inhospitable regions lacking railways and major roads, but in times of crisis the helicopters are available to the military for the whole gamut of heavy-lift tasks.

The Mi-6 design led to the Mi-l0 'Harke' flying crane helicopter of 1960. This later model was intended to carry heavy, bulky loads, and has a widespread landing gear arrangement under the slim fuselage so that a load can be brought up under the helicopter and attached to the lifting points. First flown in V-10 prototype form during 1960, the type entered service in 1962 as the Mi-10 'Harke-A'. Above the line of the cabin windows, the Mi-10 is virtually identical to the Mi-6, although without provision for the detachable wings, and in its original form used the same powerplant of two PNPP 'Aviadvigatel' (Soloviev) D-25V (TV28-M) turboshafts each rated at 5,499hp (4,100kW) that were later replaced by two 6,504hp (4,850kW) PNPP 'Aviadvigatel' (Soloviev) D-25VF turboshafts. Below this level, the depth of the fuselage is reduced considerably and the boom is deepened so that the Mi-10 offered an unbroken lower fuselage line from nose to tail. The most unusual feature of the design is the quadricycle landing gear with twin wheels on each unit: the landing gear's track is 19ft 8.75in (6.01m), and its height allows the fully fuelled helicopter to taxi forward over loads up to 12ft 3.5in (3.75m) high for attachment to the underfuselage hook. The maximum external load is 33,069lb (15,000kg) including a platform that can be attached to the inside faces of the landing gear units, and which measures 28ft 0in by 11ft 7.25in (8.53m by 3.54m) for the carriage of suitable loads. As an alternative, the Mi-10 can carry 17,637lb (8,000kg) of freight as a slung load. Freight can also be carried in the cabin, which is 46ft 0.75in (14.04m) long, 8ft 2.5in (2.50m) wide and 5ft 6in (1.68m) high.

Introduced in 1966, the Mi-10K 'Harke-B' is an improved version with shorter landing gear units, a slimmer tail pylon and, perhaps most

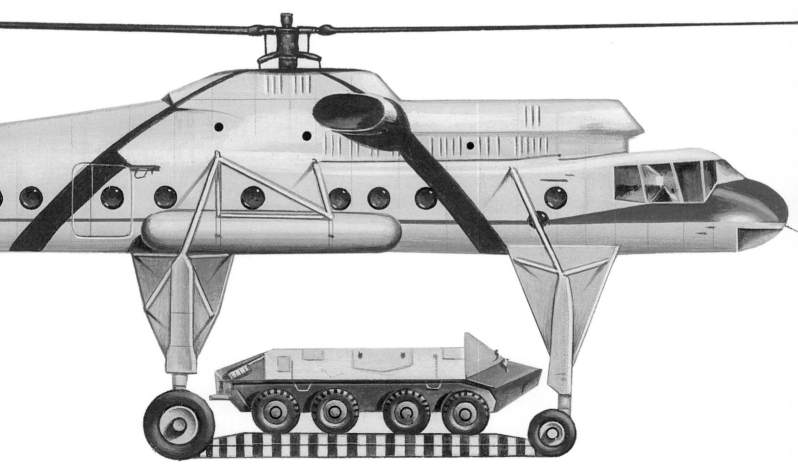

importantly of all, an undernose gondola with a rear-facing seat from which one of the two pilots can fly the helicopter in hovering flight for the loading and unloading of slung items. This improved model originally had the same powerplant as the Mi-10 and could carry a slung load of 24,250lb (11,000kg), but the retrofit of more powerful engines later improved payload to a marked degree. Production of the two types totalled some 55 helicopters up to 1977, when a small number of attrition replacement helicopters was built after a six-year break in production. Most of the Mi-10s and Mi-10Ks are operated in the resources-exploitation industry, but can be called into military service as required.

Further down the size and weight spectrum, but considerably more versatile in its tactical applications on the battlefield, is the Mi-8 that received the NATO reporting name 'Hip' and proved so successful that it has been maintained in production right up to the present in Mi-8 and improved Mi-17 variants. Basically a turbine-engined development of the piston-engined Mi-4 for civil and military applications, and flown in the first half of 1961 as the V-8 'Hip-A' prototype with a four-blade main rotor and a powerplant of one Soloviev (Ivchyenko) AI-24V turboshaft transmission-limited to 2,682hp (2,000kW), the Mi-8 was a capable machine but would clearly offer greater reliability as well as a better power-to-weight ratio with a twin-engined powerplant. The 'Hip-B' second prototype flew in September 1962 and pioneered an altogether more effective twin-turboshaft powerplant, though in this prototype form driving the same four-blade main rotor that was soon replaced by the definitive five-blade unit. Two more

Built by Aérospatiale (now Eurocopter France) as the SA. 366G Dauphin 2, this trim but somewhat underpowered search-and-rescue helicopter serves with the US Coast Guard as the HH-65A Dolphin. Other versions of the Dauphin 2 have a more directly martial application in the battlefield role with a moderately heavy weapons load.

The UH-1H is the definitive utility transport version of Bell's 'Huey' series in its single-engined form. The type still provides the ability to carry a useful number of men or light freight, but is noisy and increasingly expensive to maintain.

Despite the age of its basic design, which originated in the late 1950s for a first flight in September 1962, the Mil Mi-8 'Hip' is still the most important tactical transport helicopter operated by the Russian (originally Soviet) forces and a number of other air arms. The helicopter bears exactly the same relation to the Mi-4 'Hound' as does the Mi-2 'Hoplite' to the Mi-1 'Hare': the Mi-8 is therefore the turboshaft-powered development of the Mi-4, the prototype featuring a four-blade main rotor driven by a single 1,700hp (1,267.5kW) Soloviev turboshaft whereas the production model has a five-blade main rotor powered by two 1,700hp (1,267.5kW) Isotov TV2-117A turboshafts. The Mi-8 has a crew of three and can carry 24 troops or a freight load in the form of 8,818lb (4,000kg) carried internally or 6,616lb (3,000kg) lifted as a slung load. The type's other details include a main rotor diameter of 69ft 10.5in (21.29m), fuselage length of 59ft 7.5in (18.17m), height of 18ft 6.5in (5.65m), maximum take-off weight of 26,455lb (12,000kg), maximum speed of 161mph (260km/h) at 3,280ft (1,000m), service ceiling of 14,760ft (4,500m) and range of 276 miles (455km) with maximum payload. The two examples illustrated here are in service with the Finnish air force, and are a standard Mi-8 of the initial production civil/military series with circular cabin windows (above), and a dedicated military transport with rectangular cabin windows (below). The type is also operational with very heavy armament (unguided rockets and guided anti-tank missiles), and had also been upgraded to Mi-17 standard with an uprated dynamic system.

prototypes paved the way for the initial production model, the 'Hip-C' without the streamlined main landing gear fairings of the two prototype models. The first two models were the Mi-8P and Mi-8S with rectangular cabin windows, and were intended primarily for civil use although both saw some military service: the former was basically a convertible 28-passenger/freight transport and the latter an 11-passenger airliner. The Mi-8T 'Hip-C' was developed with a powerplant of two 1,500hp (1,118kW) TV-117 turboshafts as a utility transport with round windows and rail-mounted seats, and although developed initially for civil use was in fact built in much larger numbers for the military and with more powerful TV2-117A engines. The cabin is 7ft 8.25in (2.34m) wide and 5ft 10.75in (1.80m) high, with a length of 20ft 10.25in (6.36m) in the passenger model and 17ft 6.25in (5.34m) in the freight model, and this cabin is accessed by a large port-side forward sliding door and clamshell rear doors.

The military version has attachment points for two outrigger structures on the fuselage sides, each such structure being fitted with two hardpoints for multiple rocket launchers: these hardpoints were originally stressed for 16-tube launchers, but were later restressed for 32-tube launchers as a means of doubling the ability of the 'Hip-C' to saturate the landing zone with fire before touching down to disgorge its embarked troops. During the Mi-8's long production and service career, the Mi-8T and its successors have proved the basic concept to be excellent and highly reliable. Some of the helicopters have been upgraded to Mi-17 standard as the Mi-8MT 'Hip-C' and Mi-8MTV 'Hip-C', the latter optimised for operations under hot-and-high

Opposite top: The Aérospatiale (now Eurocopter France) SA319B Alouette III has been produced in original SA. 341 version with the 590hp (440kW) Turbomeca Astazou III turboshaft and the uprated SA. 342 version with the more powerful 870hp (649kW) Astazou XIV turboshaft. This is an example of the latter type in its SA. 342M form with an armament of four HOT tube-launched anti-tank missiles.

The Aérospatiale (now Eurocopter France) SA. 319B Alouette III Astazou was the final production model of the classic Alouette (lark) series, and is seen here in its armed form with provision under the outrigger arms for four wire-guided anti-tank missiles.

conditions with a powerplant of two 1,923hp (1,434kW) TV3-117MT turboshafts, and these are distinguishable by the relocation of the tail rotor from the starboard to the port side of the tail pylon. These two subvariants have the same weapons capability as the standard Mi-8T, but the rocket launchers are often of the B-8V20A type each carrying twenty 3.15in (80mm) S-8 unguided rockets packing a considerably heavier punch than the older 2.17in (55mm) S-5 type. There is also an Mi-8PS 'Hip-C' military VIP transport version based on the civil Mi-8 Salon executive transport.

The versatility of the Mi-8/Mi-17 series is attested by its development and production and/or conversion in a number of alternative forms. The Mi-8VZPU 'Hip-D', for example, is the airborne reserve command post version for the battlefield command and communications relay roles, and is distinguishable by its additional antenna arrays (above and below the boom) and supplementary electronic equipment carried in external box fairings attached to the hardpoints used for weapons in the 'Hip-C'.

The Mi-8TV 'Hip-F' is the export version of the 'Hip-E', with six AT-3 'Sagger' anti-tank missiles in place of the later and generally superior 'Swatters' of the Soviet type. Some of the helicopters have been further improved in capability to Mi-17 standard, and are also distinguishable by the tail rotor on the port side of the tail pylon.

The Mi-9 'Hip-G' is the airborne command post and battlefield communication relay helicopter based on the Mi-8T but distinguishable from the 'Hip-D' by detail differences such as its three 'hockey stick' antennae (two on the rear of the fuselage pod and one under the boom) and underfuselage strakes. Appearing in the early 1980s, the Mi-8SMV 'Hip-J' is an electronic warfare derivative of the basic series with a number of unspecified systems and external fittings (two box-type fairings and two 'handle' type antennae on each side of the fuselage) for the jamming of battlefield air-defence radars. Only a few such helicopters were produced, and later in the variant's career a small number were adapted for the electronic intelligence (Elint) role.

Another variant of the early 1980s, the Mi-8PPA 'Hip-K' is an advanced

ECM and communication-jamming variant with six cross-dipole antennae on each side of the rear fuselage, a large box fairing on each side of the cabin, six heat exchangers side-by-side under the fuselage for cooling of the electronic systems, but with no Doppler navigation.

The Mi-17 'Hip-H' is a much uprated and updated version of the Mi-8 that first flew in 1976 and entered service in 1981 with the dynamic system of the Mi-14, including a powerplant of two 1,925hp (1,435kW) Klimov (Isotov) TV3-117MT turboshafts and the tail rotor relocated to the port side of the fin for improved hot-and-high performance, especially in the hovering regime. The helicopter has a slightly larger cabin to facilitate carriage of the greater payload made possible by the improved powerplant, and can also carry additional weapons such as the UPK-23 gun pod containing the 23mm GSh-23L two-barrel cannon. In domestic military service this variant is generally not known as the Mi-17 but rather as the Mi-8MT or, with optimisation for operation in hot-and-high conditions, as the Mi-8MTV. Other improvements over the Mi-8TB standard include scabbed-on cockpit armour, a number of active countermeasures against IR- and radar-guided missiles, and exhaust diffusers.

The Mi-17-1 'Hip-H' version was introduced in 1989 with updated avionics and greater power in the form of two 2,072hp (1,545kW) TV3-117VM turboshafts allowing the carriage of a payload of 8,818lb (4,000kg) at altitudes up to 16,405ft (5,000m).

The Mi-17M/17V 'Hip-H' is the current production model built by the Kazan Helicopter Production Association with the same TV3-117VM powerplant as the Mi-17-1 and provision for nose radar and flotation equipment.

The Mi-17P 'Hip-K' is the Mi-17 counterpart of the Mi-8PPA and

The original Mil Mi-8 'Hip' versions are distinguishable from their later Mi-17 'Hip' offspring by a number of small features, and also by the location of the anti-torque rotor on the starboard rather than port side of the pylon extending upward and rearward from the end of the tailboom.

possesses the same NATO reporting name, but is based on the up-engined Mi-17 airframe with the Mi-8PPA's antenna array replaced by primary and secondary arrays on the rear fuselage and boom respectively. The primary array comprises a slightly concave rectangular fairing, with 32 circular antennae, on each side. The secondary array is considerably smaller and, located in line with the Doppler navigation, comprises two square fairings each containing four circular antennae.

Resulting from a programme launched in 1968 for a first prototype flight in 1973, the Mi-14PL (that received the NATO reporting name 'Haze-A') is a derivative of the Mil Mi-8 'Hip' for the considerably different land-based ASW role, with retractable landing gear (two forward-retracting single-wheel nose units and two rearward-retracting twin-wheel main units) and amphibious operating capability through the use of a boat hull and stabilizing sponsons. The planing bottom of the boat hull accommodates, from front to rear, the radome of the surveillance radar, the two nosewheel units (flanking the radome), the weapons bay, the dunking sonar (offset to starboard) and the two sonobuoy launcher tubes, while the two lateral sponsons also accommodate the main landing gear units.

The Westland (originally Saunders-Roe) Wasp HAS.Mk I seen above and below is the naval half-brother of the Scout AH.Mk I land-based model. The naval model has a slightly higher-rated powerplant, quadricycle rather than twin-skid alighting gear, a folding tail and folding main rotor blades, and naval avionics and armament for use from the quarterdeck platforms of frigates in the anti-submarine and anti-light surface vessel roles. The type has a flightcrew of two and can carry four passengers or a light freight load, and its other details include a powerplant of one 710hp (530kW) Rolls-Royce Nimbus Mk 503 turboshaft, main rotor diameter of 32ft 3in (9.83m), fuselage length of 30ft 4in (9.24m), height of 8ft 11in (2.72m), maximum take-off weight of 5,500lb (2,495kg), maximum speed of 120mph (193km/h) at sea level, service ceiling of 12,200ft (3,720m) and range of 270 miles (435km) with four passengers.

The greater demands of this exacting role dictated the introduction of an uprated powerplant, and this initially comprised two 1,700hp (1,268kW) Klimov (Isotov) TV3-117A turboshafts that were replaced in later helicopters by two 1,950hp (2,245kW) TV3-117MT turboshafts. The later helicopters also adopted a number of features of the Mi-17's dynamic system including the tail rotor switched from the starboard to the port side of the tail pylon, introduction of an externally mounted winch above the port-side sliding cabin door, and omission of the doors of the landing gear bays. The type can also be used in the SAR role with armament replaced by a rescue winch and other mission equipment.

In 1989 an improved variant was introduced as the Mi-14PLM with a number of detail improvements including a MAD installation.

The Mi-14BT 'Haze-B' is the mine countermeasures version of the 'Haze-A', identifiable by the strake and blister fairing (the former containing hydraulic tubing and the latter accommodating the relocated cabin heating and ventilation system) on the starboard side of the fuselage. The type can tow three different types of sled for the detonation of magnetic, acoustic and impact mines, and is visually differentiated from the Mi-14PL by its lack of the towed MAD 'bird' and by the windows installed in the

extreme rear of the fuselage pod to allow the mine counter measures (MCM) operator to keep watch on his towed equipment.

The Mi-14PS 'Haze-C' is the dedicated three-crew SAR variant of the 'Haze-B', retaining the starboard-side strake and pod but introducing a double-size door on the port side together with a retractable rescue winch with a three-person basket. The variant carries ten 20-person life-rafts, and the cabin is outfitted for the carriage of two litters and eight seated survivors. Other notable features of the Mi-14PS are its three searchlights and its ability to tow life-rafts containing survivors.

One of the best British designs appeared in 1958 in the form of the Westland Wasp/Scout evolutionary development of the Saunders-Roe P.531 prototype. A light general-purpose type, the helicopter was adopted by the Royal Navy as an anti-submarine helicopter and liaison machine with tricycle landing gear and the name Wasp, and by the army as an observation, liaison and light anti-tank type with twin-skid landing gear and the name Scout.

The same year also saw the appearance of the Kaman K-600, the first American helicopter powered by twin turboshafts. A general-purpose type, the K-600 was built in some numbers as the H-43 Huskie for the USAF, whose primary use for the type was to rescue the crews of aircraft involved in take-off and landing accidents.

Although developed for the Royal Navy, the Westland Wasp HAS.Mk I is now operated only by navies with have received ex-British 'Leander' class frigates or their Dutch-built counterparts of the 'Van Speijk' class.

The Kaman SH-2 Seasprite that first flew in 1959 was the world's first truly all-round helicopter, with the excellent speed of 155mph (250km/h) and a range of 450 miles (724km). The importance of the SH-2 lies in design features such as its retractable landing gear and watertight fuselage bottom, allowing the machine to sit in the sea, deceiving enemy submarines into thinking it had left the area, and making rescue operations easier. With advanced avionics and flying systems, the SH-2 has all-weather capability and can serve as an anti-missile defence when fitted with the appropriate electronics. The SH-2 was steadily upgraded in capabilities, and is still widely employed by the US Navy in its SH-2F Seasprite and SH-2G Super Seasprite twin-engined models.

The origins of the type can be traced back to 1956, when the US Navy issued a requirement for a high-performance utility helicopter capable of all-weather operations from smaller surface warships for the fulfilment of the whole range of utility missions. The most important of these roles was shipborne SAR, but other significant missions were planeguard, gunfire observation, reconnaissance, liaison, communications, vertical replenishment ('vertrep'), of ships at sea, casevac, and wirelaying for tactical air controller operations.

Kaman won the resulting design competition with its K-20 concept, which was a rarity among Kaman's designs in being a helicopter of conventional layout with a single main rotor and thus a longer rear fuselage supporting a small anti-torque rotor. Other features were tailwheel landing gear with retractable main units to facilitate the use of the rescue hoist that was one of the type's most important items of equipment, and a watertight hull so that the type could alight on the sea. The US Navy ordered four YHU2K-1 (from 1962 YUH-2A) prototypes, and the first of these flew in July 1959 with a crew of two, a payload that could include 12 passengers or two litters and four seated casualties, and a powerplant of one 1,025hp (764kW) General Electric T58-GE-6 turboshaft derated to 875hp (652kW). Flight trials confirmed that the K-20 could be a very capable helicopter, and the type was ordered into production with an uprated powerplant in the form of the 1,250hp (932kW) T58-GE-8 turboshaft.

The Kaman H-2 Seasprite has been developed through several versions initially with a single engine and then with two in variants of steadily more impressive multi-role capability. The type is still in service in two light airborne multi-purpose system (LAMPS) Mk I variants that provide the frigates and older destroyers of the US Navy with a helicopter that can undertake the anti-missile warning, anti-submarine, anti-light surface vessel, rescue and utility transport roles. Seen here is an SH-2D upgraded to SH-2F standard with a crew of three, powerplant of two 1,350hp (1,007kW) General Electric T58-GE-8F turboshafts, main rotor diameter of 44ft 0in (13.41m), overall length of 52ft 7in (16.03m), height of 15ft 6in (4.72m), maximum take-off weight of 13,500lb (6,123kg), maximum speed of 150mph (241km/h) at sea level, service ceiling of 22,500ft (6,860m) and range of 431 miles (695km).

Orders for this HU2K-1 initial production model totalled 84 helicopters
that entered service from December 1962, by which time the designation
had been altered to UH-2A. Ordered with the designation HU2K-1U (that
had been altered before the type entered service), the UH-2B was a
simplified version of the UH-2A and lacked all-weather flight capability.
Production totalled 104 helicopters, most of which were later upgraded to
UH-2A all-weather standard without any change in their designation.

In March 1965, Kaman completed a Seasprite conversion with a twin-
engined powerplant. The use of two T58-GE-8B turboshafts, each rated at
1,250hp (932kW) and driving a transmission limited to a combined rating
of 1,685hp (1,256kW), improved flight performance and, perhaps more
importantly, enhanced safety in over-water operations as each engine was
individually able to support the helicopter in level flight. The conversion
caught the attention of the US Navy, which in 1966 ordered the similar
alteration of two UH-2Bs to the UH-2C twin-engined standard for prototype
trials. These confirmed the success of the revised powerplant, and many
UH-2As and UH-2Bs were then converted to UH-2C standard for
redelivery from August 1967 with a pair of T58-GE-8B turboshafts, slightly
more tail area, and minor alterations of the cockpit and main rotor pylon.
Many of the converted helicopters were later re-engined with two 1,350hp
(1,007kW) T58-GE-8F turboshafts.

Another six UH-2As were converted to HH-2C Seasprite standard for the combat SAR role in the Vietnam War. These machines had a powerplant of two T58-GE-8F turboshafts, a more advanced main rotor, a four- rather than three-blade tail rotor, and twin- rather than single-wheel main landing gear units for operation at a higher maximum take-off weight. Other features were self-sealing fuel tankage, armour protection for the crew, a more advanced rescue hoist, and armament in the form of an undernose turret mounting one 0.3in (7.62mm) General Electric GAU-2B/A Minigun rotary six-barrel machine gun, and two 0.3in M60 machine guns pintle-mounted in the cabin doors. From February 1970, another 70 UH-2As were redelivered after conversion to the HH-2D standard that approximated that of the HH-2C except for its lack of armour and armament.

In the late 1960s the US Navy became increasingly concerned about the inadequacy of its anti-submarine and anti-ship missile defence capabilities at a time when the USSR was introducing several improved nuclear-powered attack submarine classes and specialised anti-ship missiles. Kaman proposed a development of its Seasprite to meet the resulting light airborne multi-purpose system (LAMPS) Mk I requirement, and the US Navy agreed that the type would make a useful interim type to operate from the helicopter facilities of its destroyers and frigates. In 1971, therefore, two HH-2Ds were modified to SH-2D standard with search radar using

an antenna in an undernose radome, an electronic support measures (ESM) system for the detection of possible threats through their electro-magnetic emissions, removable MAD system (with its sensor in a towed 'bird') on the starboard side of the fuselage and balanced by a port-side launcher for 15 sonobuoys, the associated displays and controls, and provision for armament in the form of two Mk 46 lightweight torpedoes.

The first of the two prototype conversions flew in March 1971. These conversions proved highly successful, and the US Navy therefore ordered the conversion of another 18 machines to a similar interim standard as Kaman completed work on the definitive LAMPS Mk I type that was now clearly available on the basis of the Seasprite. The SH-2Ds had all been delivered by March 1972.

Two HH-2Ds were later converted as YSH-2E prototypes to meet the full LAMPS Mk I requirement with improved radar and updated systems, and the first of these machines flew in March 1972. The planned SH-2E production model did not come to fruition, however, for the US Navy opted instead for the SH-2F improved version of the SH-2D with greater power, strengthened landing gear with the tailwheel moved farther forward, and a titanium rotor hub. The SH-2F entered service in May 1973 as the definitive LAMPS Mk I helicopter for the anti-submarine, anti-ship missile defence, SAR, and utility transport roles, tasks in which the SH-2F still offers capabilities unmatched in any helicopter of comparable size. The initial SH-2F fleet comprised 88 UH-2A, UH-2B and UH-2C conversions effected between 1973 and 1982, and this force was supplemented by 16 SH-2D conversions with a higher maximum take-off weight.

So successful did the SH-2F prove, moreover, that there was demand for greater numbers and the SH-2F fleet was therefore expanded by 54 new

helicopters built between 1985 and 1989. The new-build SH-2F differs from the SH-2G principally in its maximum ordnance load of 1,200lb (544kg) and powerplant of two 1,350hp (1,007kW) T58-GE-8F turboshafts driving an improved main rotor. The SH-2Fs still in US Navy service are being upgraded to virtual SH-2G standard with improved avionics and General Electric T700-GE-401 turboshafts for better performance (in terms of range and reliability) and greater commonality with the Sikorsky SH-60B Seahawk.

For service in the Persian Gulf since 1987, some 16 SH-2Fs were upgraded in defensive capability by the installation of an ESM system with rear-warning radar (RWR), ECM and passive targeting capabilities, two chaff/flare/decoy dispensers, one IR jammer, one missile warning system, one missile warning and jamming system and, under the nose, one forward-looking IR (FLIR) sensor.

The SH-2G Super Seasprite is a significantly improved SH-2F with a powerplant of two 1,723hp (1,285kW) T700-GE-401 turboshafts driving a new and slightly larger main rotor with composite-structure rotor blades. The variant also introduced a digital databus for full integration of the modern sensor and data processing systems, which include a much-enhanced acoustic data processor, an updated tactical navigation system, a global positioning system (GPS) receiver, an acoustic system data link, an FLIR sensor, improved ESM and dunking sonar. The prototype was a converted SH-2F that flew as an engine test bed in April 1985 and with full electronics in December 1989. The new type entered service in 1991 in the form of six new-build helicopters and a planned 97 examples converted from SH-2F standard but, in the event, the end of the 'Cold War' reduced the US Navy's requirement and only 17 'production' conversions were effected to complement the prototype conversion. The US Navy is to upgrade its in-service SH-2Gs with the improved defensive features of the SH-2Fs operated

Above: Westland developed its Sea King from the Sikorsky SH-3 with more sophisticated mission electronics, and the initial model was the Sea King HAS.Mk I illustrated here.

Above right: The Sea King HAS.Mk 5 is a considerably more capable anti-submarine helicopter than the Sea King HAS.Mk I, with more advanced sensors and processing equipment carried in a larger tactical compartment.

Left: The most important assault transport helicopter available to the US Marine Corps is the Sikorsky CH-53 Sea Stallion and Super Stallion series, which had been developed through a number of variants with two or three engines. This is an example of the definitive twin-engined model, the CH-53D.

in the Persian Gulf, together with the Magic Lantern-30 laser system for the detection of underwater mines. Kaman also offers the type in the anti-shipping role with stub wings for the carriage of AGM-65D Maverick ASMs, and is actively marketing rebuilds of up to 72 SH-2F helicopters now surplus to US Navy requirements.

Evermore advanced ideas reached the hardware stage during the late 1950s, and in 1960 the important Sikorsky S-61 emerged from the experimental shops. The type soon entered service with the US Navy as the SH-3 Sea King with a powerplant of two General Electric T58 turboshafts. The Sea King was of great operational importance at the time of its introduction as the world's first all-weather helicopter effectively combining the submarine hunter-killer roles that had previously required the efforts of two helicopters, one to hunt with sonar and the other to kill with depth charges and/or homing torpedoes; the US Coast Guard deploys a variant of the same basic type as a patrol and rescue helicopter. The USAF used the same basic airframe for transport missions and for rescuing aircraft and their crews, although these CH-3 and HH-3 Jolly Green Giant helicopters had a revised fuselage with retractable tricycle landing gear, a ventral ramp/door arrangement, and features such as improved armament and self-sealing fuel tanks. There were also two S-61 civil variants that secured modest but useful orders for the airliner and resources-exploitation support industries.

The S-61 was designed in the later 1950s to meet a US Navy requirement for an ASW helicopter to replace the Sikorsky HSS-1 Seabat, and combined, for the first time in such a machine, the hunter and the killer capabilities that previously required the teaming of two less capable helicopters. The transition to this more effective dual capability was made possible by the availability of the General Electric T58 turboshaft, which was a compact engine offering a considerably lower vibration level and also a very much higher power-to-weight ratio than any comparable piston engine. The incorporation of such an engine into the S-61 therefore resulted in a design that was somewhat different in conceptual terms from that of the S-58. This difference was reflected not so much in the basic configuration, which was little altered except for its full amphibious capability, but rather in the feasibility of a more reliable twin-turboshaft powerplant. This opened the way for the S-58's nose-mounted single piston engine to be replaced by two turboshafts located above the fuselage in positions flanking the gearbox and transmission for the five-blade main and tail rotors. This installation above the hold obviated the need for the S-58's long, heavy and obstructive transmission shaft and thus opened the way for a fuselage with greater useful capacity. Other notable features of the new design were a boat hull for emergency waterborne capability with stability enhanced by the outrigger sponsons that provided accommodation for the main units of the retractable tricycle landing gear, far greater payload, and provision for a more sophisticated mission suite in the hold, which was occupied by two sonar operators.

The specific variant for the US Navy was evolved as the S-61B, and the US Navy's go-ahead was signed in December 1957. The initial 10 machines were YHSS-2 prototype and service test helicopters, and the first of these flew in March 1959 with a powerplant of two 1,050hp (783kW) T58-GE-6 turboshafts. Evaluation of these helicopters confirmed the radical superiority of the S-61B over the S-58. This type was ordered into production as the HSS-2 Sea King (from 1962 SH-3A), with provision for an external payload of 6,000lb (2,722kg) carried on a sling with automatic touch-down release capability, mission equipment that included dunking sonar and an

Seen here in the form of a Sea King HAS.Mk 1, the Westland Sea King offers capabilities superior to those of its American SH-3 Sea King original by possessing the onboard tactical processing equipment that allows autonomous rather than ship-controlled anti-submarine operations. The radome to the rear of the powerplant/main rotor assembly covers the antenna for the Ekco AW391 surveillance radar that was replaced in the Sea King HAS.Mk 5 and later versions by the Marconi Sea Search radar.

autostabilization system providing for automatic transition to and from the hover as well as automatic altitude hold for effective sonar operation, and a powerplant of two T58-GE-6 turboshafts that were soon changed for two 1,250hp (932kW) T58-GE-8 or -8B turboshafts.

Production totalled 245 helicopters that entered service from September 1961. Numbers of SH-3A helicopters were later converted for different tasks, and these included three examples of the CH-3A for the USAF's role of supplying 'Texas Tower' radar outposts in the Atlantic; 12 examples of the HH-3A for the combat SAR role with T58-GE-8F engines, a 0.3in (7.62mm) General Electric GAU-2B/A Minigun rotary six-barrel machine gun in a barbette in the rear of each sponson, armour protection and provision for long-range fuel tanks; nine examples of the RH-3A for the exacting mine countermeasures role with the ASW equipment replaced by towed MCM equipment; and eight examples of the VH-3A for the presidential and VIP transport role. There were also three CH-3B conversions generally similar to the CH-3As and used for the same role. A total of 41 helicopters to SH-3A standard was produced for Canada (four built in the USA and the other 37 assembled in Canada) with the designation CHSS-2 that was later altered to CH-124.

The USAF was highly impressed with the capabilities of the ex-US Navy helicopters converted to S-61A amphibious transport standard with the designations CH-3A and CH-3B, and decided to procure a variant fully optimised for its particular requirements. Sikorsky developed this as the S-61R with a powerplant of two 1,300hp (969kW) turboshafts, an auxiliary power unit for independence from ground facilities, pressurised rotor blades for simple and quick inspection, a simplified lower hull, lateral fuselage sponsons into which the main units of the revised tricycle landing gear units

The original SH-3A Sea King version of the Sikorsky S-61 anti-submarine helicopter for the US Navy was austerely equipped for its primary task with just dunking sonar and an armament of depth charges or two homing torpedoes.

retracted, and the type of pod-and-boom fuselage that allowed the incorporation of a hydraulically-powered ventral ramp/door giving direct access to the hold, which was 25ft 10.5in (7.89m) long, 6ft 6in (1.98m) wide and 6ft 3in (1.91m) high, fitted with a winch for cargo handling, and additionally accessed by a jettisonable sliding door on the forward port side of the hold. The type was delivered from December 1963, and a total of 133 helicopters was ordered although only the first 41 were actually delivered to this initial standard, and the eventual production total, including the CH-3E, reached only 83.

Delivered from June 1966, the SH-3D was an improved ASW version with more powerful 1,400hp (1,044kW) T58-GE-10 turboshafts and improved dunking sonar. The US Navy ordered 73 such helicopters, and others were built for export. The type had a maximum official warload capability of 840lb (626kg) in the form of depth charges or two Mk 46 homing torpedoes, but the type had the ability to carry a slung load of 8,000lb (3,629kg), so the warload could be considerably higher than the quoted figure. The only current variant of this model in US Navy service is the VH-3D VIP transport, of which 11 were produced as SH-3D conversions.

The CH-3E was the improved standard introduced from the forty-second machine of the USAF's order for the CH-3. This was characterised by the introduction of a significantly more capable powerplant comprising two 1,500hp (1,132kW) T58-GE-5 turboshafts that was later retrofitted in the CH-3C. This uprated type was delivered from February 1966, and could lift 25 troops, or 15 litters, or a freight load of 5,000lb (2,268kg) internally or 8,000lb (3,629kg) externally, although a more important role was combat SAR in the Vietnam War with a powerful rescue hoist. For this difficult task, each helicopter was fitted with armament for the self-defence and fire-suppression roles: this armament comprised one Emerson TAT-102 turret

Above: The large cabin of the Westland Sea King is generally outfitted as a tactical compartment for the implementation of the whole anti-submarine task, but can be stripped out to turn the helicopter into a casualty evacuation machine of considerable capability.

on the outer end of each sponson and remotely controlled from sighting stations in the port and starboard personnel doors; each TAT-102 turret carried one 0.3in (7.62mm) General Electric GAU-2B/A Minigun rotary six-barrel machine gun with 8,000 rounds, and the combination of the turrets' positions and ability to traverse through an arc of more than 180 degrees meant that 360-degree fire capability was possible, with overlapping fields of fire toward the nose.

Service in Vietnam indicated the need for greater operational capabilities, and this led to the development of the HH-3E Jolly Green Giant, based on the armed CH-3E but fitted with protective armour, self-sealing fuel tanks, a retractable inflight-refuelling probe, jettisonable external tanks, a high-speed hoist, and other specialised equipment. Some 14 of the type were ordered, but only eight were completed as such and the total was boosted by the conversion of all the CH-3Es to this standard.

The designation HH-3F Pelican is applied to 40 of the US Coast Guard SAR version of the CH-3E, delivered from 1968 with search radar (using an antenna in a nose radome offset to port), a waterproofed fuselage, and provision for 15 litters and six seated survivors.

Under the SH-3G designation, 105 SH-3As and SH-3Ds were converted to utility helicopter standard with ASW equipment that can be removed to allow the installation of additional fuel tankage and seating for up to 15 passengers.

The SH-3H is the multi-role version of the SH-3G for the dual anti-submarine warfare and anti-ship missile defence roles, with upgraded ASW equipment including dunking sonar, active/passive sonobuoys and MAD gear with a towed 'bird' carried under the starboard stabilizing float, as well as specialist equipment including high-performance radar and a radar warning receiver for the fleet missile defence role, whose primary task is the detection and localisation of incoming anti-ship missiles. Some 112 SH-3As, SH-3Ds and SH-3Gs were upgraded to this standard.

Opposite Top; The Westland Sea King HC.Mk 4 is the primary assault transport helicopter for the delivery of Royal Marines in amphibious operations, and is a hybrid type that combines the folding tail and main rotor blades of the Sea King with the modified fuselage and landing gear of the Commando developed by Westland as a land-based tactical transport version of the Sea King.

The Westland Sea King Mk 45 is the version of the Sea King series for the Pakistani navy, with provision for the carriage and firing of the powerful AM.39 Exocet anti-ship missile.

Although developed for the German navy as a search-and-rescue type, the Westland Sea King Mk 41 has since been upgraded to full combat capability with Ferranti Seaspray search radar and an armament of two or four Kormoran heavyweight anti-ship missiles.

A development of the piston-engined S-52, the turboshaft-powered S-59 did not enter service, but was useful in the development of features such as turboshaft propulsion and retractable landing gear to give helicopters higher speeds.

The S-61A is the amphibious transport version of the Sea King for the export market, and is able to carry 26 troops, or 15 litters, or 12 VIPs, or a comparatively substantial freight load. The S-61D is the export variant of the SH-3D Sea King.

The Sea King has also been produced under licence in other countries, notably Italy, Japan and the UK. The Agusta (Sikorsky) ASH-3D is the Italian licence-built version of the SH-3D anti-submarine helicopter, differing only slightly from the original in items such as airframe strengthening, a revised tailplane and an uprated powerplant. The ASH-3D also has modified armament and avionics, the former including up to four Mk 46 torpedoes, each weighing 515lb (234kg), or two large anti-ship missiles, and the latter including SMA APS-705 surveillance radar or SMA APS-706 radar when the helicopter is fitted with the Marte Mk II system for Sea Killer Mk 2 anti-ship missiles. The ASH-3H is the Italian licence-built version of the SH-3H Sea King with role optimisation for anti-submarine and anti-ship warfare. The type can also lift a freight load of 6,000lb (2,722kg) carried internally or 8,000lb (3,629kg) carried externally as a slung load. Other tasks undertaken by the ASH-3H, which is fitted with dunking sonar as well as SMA APS-707 surveillance radar with its antenna in a chin radome, are anti-ship missile defence, early warning (EW) and tactical trooping. There is also an AS-61R SAR version of this helicopter, basically equivalent to the American HH-3F Pelican.

The Mitsubishi (Sikorsky) HSS-2 is the Japanese licence-built version of the SH-3A, and the Japanese company produced a total of 185 such helicopters including the HSS-2A and HSS-2B upgraded versions equivalent to the SH-3D and SH-3H respectively.

The Westland Sea King is the British licence-built version of the H-3 series. In 1959, Westland secured a licence not only to build but also to undertake further development of the S-61, but it was not until well into the following decade that Westland began to take advantage of this licence in the creation of a helicopter optimised for the Royal Navy's requirement for an advanced type to succeed the Westland Wessex as a shipborne anti-submarine helicopter with fully autonomous search-and-destroy capability over long ranges/endurances.

The first of four helicopters assembled from Sikorsky-supplied components flew in September 1967, and the success of these machines paved the way for the first British-built Sea King HAS.Mk 1 that flew in May 1969, leading the way for a service debut in February 1970 with a powerplant of two licence-built General Electric T58 turboshafts in the form of a pair of Rolls-Royce (Bristol Siddeley) Gnome H.1400 turboshafts each rated at 1,500hp (1,118kW) for take-off and 1,250hp (932kW) for continuous running. This variant was considerably better-equipped for the operational role than the baseline American model, and its avionics included surveillance radar with its antenna in a dorsal radome, dunking sonar and Doppler navigation, while its primary weapon options were up to four Mk 44 lightweight torpedoes or four Mk 11 depth charges. Production of the Sea King HAS.Mk 1 totalled 56 helicopters. There followed the Sea King HAS.Mk 2, which was a simple derivative of the Sea King HAS.Mk 1 but with a powerplant of two 1,660hp (1,238kW) Gnome H.1400-1 turboshafts and a number of features developed for Australia's Sea King Mk 50. Production totalled 21 helicopters, and all surviving Sea King HAS.Mk 1s were upgraded to the same standard with the designation Sea King HAS.Mk 2A. The model's cabin is 19ft 3in (5.87m) long in the ASW version, increasing to 24ft 11in (7.59m) in the SAR version, and its width and height are 5ft 6in (1.98m) and 6ft 3.5in (1.92m) respectively.

The designation Sea King AEW.Mk 2A is used for 10 Sea King HAS.Mk 2s converted to the AEW role with the Thorn EMI Searchwater low-altitude surveillance task (LAST) radar. This uses a 360-degree scan antenna in a pressurised radome on a swivelling arm attached to the starboard side of the fuselage: the arm and radome are turned to the rear for carrier operations and cruising flight, then swivelled down to the vertical position below the fuselage for patrol operations. In 1992 it was revealed that the helicopters

The Sikorsky HH-3E was developed from the US Air Force's CH-3 land-based transport version of the US Navy's SH-3 Sea King maritime anti-submarine helicopter, as a combat search-and-rescue helicopter for use in the recovery of aircrew whose warplanes had been forced down in hostile territory during the Vietnam War. The type soon became known as the 'Jolly Green Giant', and features that suited the type to its more intensive operational role were uprated engines, armour protection, an armament of two 0.3in (7.62mm) Minigun six-barrel rotary machine guns, additional fuel capacity, an extending inflight-refuelling probe, and a high-capacity rescue hoist with a weighted penetrator to reach the ground through a jungle canopy.

are to be upgraded electronically with the Searchwater radar modified to incorporate pulse-Doppler capability.

The Sea King HAR.Mk 3 is the dedicated SAR derivative of the Sea King HAS.Mk 2 for the RAF, which received 19 of the type for service from 1977 with no anti-submarine equipment but with additional avionics. The cabin is outfitted for the carriage of two dedicated mission crew (electronics/winch operator and loadmaster/winchman) and 19 seated survivors, or two litters and 11 seated survivors, or six litters. A subsequent order for six Sea King HAR.Mk 3A helicopters with improved avionics raised the Sea King HAR.Mk 3 variant's total to 25 machines.

The Sea King HC.Mk 4 is the assault transport version of the Commando Mk 2 (see below) for the Royal Marines, with the folding rotors of the Sea King series and able to carry 28 troops or 6,000lb (2,272kg) of freight internally, or alternatively a slung load of 8,000lb (3,629kg). The type is equipped for the troops to make parachute or

abseiling departure. The initial order covered 17 helicopters delivered from 1980, but subsequent orders raised the total to 40.

The Sea King HAS.Mk 5 is a much-upgraded ASW and SAR variant of the Sea King HAS.Mk 2 for the Royal Navy, with advanced sensors and data-processing capability in a cabin enlarged by the rearward movement of the aft bulkhead by 5ft 7.75in (1.72m). The variant's electronics include Thorn EMI ARI.5991 Sea Searcher surveillance radar, improved dunking sonar, mini-sonobuoys, and the AQS-902C LAPADS acoustic data processing and tactical display system. The Sea Searcher radar has a rotating antenna in a larger radome, and provides twice the range of the HAS.Mk 2's AW.391 type as well as better discrimination against ECM, while the LAPADS (updated in the late 1980s to AQS-902G-DS standard for improved operational capability) allows faster and more accurate processing of data from the dunking sonar and sonobuoys. Some 30 such helicopters were delivered between October 1980 and July 1986, and further helicopters of the same standard were provided by the update of 56 older machines (one Sea King HAS.Mk 1, 20 Sea King HAS.Mk 2 and 35 Sea King HAS.Mk 2A helicopters). In 1987 and 1988, four of the helicopters, with their anti-submarine electronics removed, were transferred to the RAF as Sea King HAR.Mk 5 SAR machines.

The Sea King AEW.Mk 5 designation is applied to three Sea King HAS.Mk 5 helicopters converted to the AEW role in a standard basically similar to that of the Sea King AEW.Mk 2 with Thomson Thorn Searchwater surveillance radar.

This view highlights the main features of the Westland Sea King with its boat-hulled fuselage, float-shaped stabilizing sponsons accommodating the retractable main units of the tailwheel landing gear, the carriage of homing torpedoes on the rear fuselage, the use of the main part of the fuselage for crew (flightcrew of two on the forward flightdeck and mission crew of two in the well-equipped central fuselage tactical compartment) and mission equipment including search radar and dunking sonar, and the powerplant of two Rolls-Royce Gnome turboshafts side-by-side ahead of the main rotor assembly.

Delivered between January and August 1990 to the extent of five helicopters, the Sea King HAS.Mk 6 is an improved version of the Sea King HAS.Mk 5 based on the Advanced Sea King concept. The variant has the AQS-902G-DS integrated acoustic data processing system (with inputs to cathode-ray tube displays from sonobuoys and GEC Ferranti Type 2069 dunking sonar, which is the older Plessey Type 195 with digital signal processing and the ability to operate at depths down to about 700ft/213m) in place of the original 'stand-alone' AQS-902C acoustic data processing system and analogue-processed Type 195 sonar able to operate to a depth of 245ft (75m), improved radar, an internal MAD system, enhanced ESM, provision for two Sea Eagle anti-ship missiles, a strengthened fuselage, a powerplant of two 1,660hp (1,238kW) Gnome H.1400-1T turboshafts transmission-limited to a combined maximum of 2,950hp (2,200kW), an uprated dynamic system including composite-structure blades on both the main and improved tail rotors, an unbraced stabilizer, and increased internal fuel capacity. The Royal Navy's force of Sea King HAS.Mk 6 helicopters is being enlarged by the conversion of older Sea King helicopters to this standard. The first step was the upgrade of 26 Sea King HAS.Mk 5s (one of them as a prototype for the new standard), and another 44 conversion kits have been ordered.

The designation Sea King AEW.Mk 7 is proposed for an upgrade of the Sea King AEW.Mk 2 for service from the year 2000, with improved surveillance radar (the Thomson Thorn Searchwater 2000 and GEC-Marconi Blue Vixen being the competing types), a joint tactical information distribution system (JTIDS) data link, and a new central tactical system with coloured displays.

Moderately large numbers of Sea King helicopters have been delivered to the air forces and navies of British allies, and the type has also been sold in modest numbers as a land-based tactical helicopter with the revised name Commando, with its payload/range and endurance capabilities optimised for the trooping, freighting, logistic support, and casevac primary roles, with air-to-surface attack and SAR as important secondary roles. The type's most obvious external differences are stub wings (in place of the Sea King's stabilizing sponson floats) and non-retractable tailwheel landing gear. The hold is 24ft 11in (7.59m) long, 6ft 6in (1.98m) wide and 6ft 3.5in (1.93m) high, and access to the hold is provided by a port-side airstair door at the front and a starboard-side cargo door at the rear.

The Commando first flew in September 1973 with a powerplant of two Gnome H.1400 turboshafts, and the designation Commando Mk 1 is used for five helicopters delivered from January 1974 to the Egyptian air force for the trooping role with accommodation for 21 troops. The Commando Mk 2 was first flown in January 1975 and built as the major version of the Commando series. It is an uprated version of the Commando Mk 1 with Gnome H.1400-1 turboshafts and a hold able to accommodate 28 men or 6,000lb (2,722kg) of freight. Saudi Arabia funded the purchase of 17 such troop transports for the Egyptian air force, and other deliveries included three Commando Mk 2A 15-passenger VIP transports for the Qatari air force, two Commando Mk 2B 15-passenger VIP transports for the Egyptian air force, one Commando Mk 2C improved 15-passenger VIP transport for the Qatari air force, and four Commando Mk 2E Elint and jamming helicopters for the Egyptian air force. The Commando Mk 3, of which eight were delivered to Qatar between December 1982 and January 1984, is an armed multi-role version with sponsons.

The Soviet counterpart to the Sea King, although built in considerably fewer numbers, is the Kamov Ka-25, which remains a classic example of the modern helicopter with co-axial contra-rotating main rotor units. The Ka-25 was designed to counter the American development of nuclear-powered

The version of the Sikorsky S-61 used by the US Coast Guard for the search-and-rescue mission is the HH-3F Pelican, which is in essence a version of the HH-3E 'Jolly Green Giant' without the features required for long-range penetration of hostile airspace.

The designation HH-3A was used for 12 Sikorsky SH-3A Sea King helicopters converted as interim combat search-and-rescue machines pending the arrival of the first HH-3E 'Jolly Green Giant' helicopters.

submarines carrying nuclear-tipped ballistic missiles (SSBNs) in the mid-1950s, which clearly threatened to upset the balance of power between the USA and the USSR in favour of the Americans. The USSR decided that the American SSBN capability would have to be counterbalanced by a Soviet SSBN force, but this was a longer-term solution to a problem that had to be addressed immediately. A factor working for the Soviets was the comparatively short range of the Lockheed UGM-27 Polaris first-generation submarine-launched ballistic missile (SLBM), which meant that American SSBNs had initially to operate in waters fairly close to the USSR's maritime frontiers if they were to strike at strategic targets deep in the Soviet heartlands.

This opened the possibility that Soviet submarines and surface warships could engage and destroy the SSBNs if they had the right sensors to detect their large targets. A far-ranging programme was therefore launched in 1957, and included the advanced anti-submarine helicopter fitted with modern sensors and weapons. Such a helicopter could operate from comparatively small and unsophisticated surface vessels, using its range and speed to extend the search and attack radius far beyond that of the parent vessel.

The resulting helicopter, introduced to service in 1965, was the Ka-25 (NATO reporting name 'Hormone') that was clearly derived from the Ka-20 'Harp' twin-turboshaft prototype revealed in 1961 and itself developed on the conceptual basis of the Ka-15 'Hen' and Ka-18 'Hog' piston-engined helicopters.

The Ka-25 is thus of typical Kamov configuration with superimposed co-axial rotors turning in opposite directions so that the torque reaction of each three-blade rotor cancels that of the other and thereby removes the need for an anti-torque rotor at the tail, which can thus be made shorter with consequent advantages in shipboard hangarage requirements. In other respects, the Ka-25PL 'Hormone-A' initial model has a large fuselage with a conventional tail unit carrying triple vertical surfaces, quadricycle landing gear, a powerplant of two 888hp (662kW) OMKB 'Mars' (Glushenkov) GTD-3F or, in later helicopters, two 896hp (735kW) GTD-3BM turboshafts located close to the main gearbox above the cabin roof, and the combination of the volume and weight-lifting capabilities for a mass of electronic equipment as well as weapons carried in an internal bay.

The Ka-25PL is the dedicated ASW version of the series with a cabin 12ft 11.5in (3.95m) long, 4ft 11in (1.50m) wide and 4ft 1.25in (1.25m) high accessed by a sliding door on the port side. The primary failing of this

variant is lack of any automatic hover capability, which prevents it from using its dunking sonar in night and adverse-weather operations. The Ka-25BShZ 'Hormone-A' is a derivative of the Ka-25PL designed to tow minesweeping equipment and therefore not fitted with sonar equipment.

The Ka-25T 'Hormone-B' is the missile support version of the Ka-25 family, fitted with data-link equipment for the provision of targeting data and the mid-course updating of long-range anti-ship missiles such as the SS-N-3 'Shaddock', SS-N-12 'Sandbox', SS-N-19 'Shipwreck' and SS-N-22 'Sunburn' weapons launched by major surface ships. This variant is distinguishable from the Ka-25PL by the domed undersurface of the nose radome for its 'Big Bulge' radar and the provision of a different radar with a cylindrical radome under the rear of the cabin. All four units of the landing gear can be retracted to reduce interference to the radar.

The Ka-25PS 'Hormone-C' is the utility and SAR variant of the Ka-25 family, without the offensive avionics and armament of the 'Hormone-A' but often carrying a rescue hoist and other specialist gear as well as equipment for mid-course update of ship-launched anti-ship missiles.

The Ka-25 series has now been supplanted on the more advanced warships of the Russian navy by the Ka-27 'Helix' series of helicopters. Designed from 1969 as successor to the Ka-25 'Hormone' series with improvements such as the ability to operate the dunking sonar at night and

One of the most important tactical transport helicopters in Western service, the Aérospatiale AS 332B Puma (now Eurocopter France AS 532 Cougar) carries a crew of up to three as well as a payload of 21 troops, or six litters and seven seated casualties, or 8,818lb (4,000kg) of freight in the cabin or 9,921lb (4,500kg) of freight as a slung load. Other details include a powerplant of two 1,877hp (1,400kW) Turbomeca Makila IA1 turboshafts, main rotor diameter of 51ft 2.2in (15.60m), fuselage length of 48ft 5in (14.76m), height of 16ft 1.75in (4.92m), maximum take-off weight of 20,613lb (9,350kg), maximum speed of 163mph (262km/h) at sea level, service ceiling of 13,450ft (4,100m) and range of 384 miles (618km).

in adverse weather, the Ka-27 retains the earlier type's configuration with superimposed co-axial rotors to obviate the need for a long tail carrying an anti-torque rotor. The 'Helix' first flew in prototype form during 1973. Compared with the Ka-25, the Ka-27 has considerably greater power from its two 2,205hp (1,645kW) Klimov (Isotov) TV3-117V turboshafts and slightly greater dimensions for much enhanced performance and payload within an airframe still able to fit into the same shipboard hangar as the Ka-25. The Ka-27PL 'Helix-A' is the dedicated ASW variant of the series, and was introduced to service in 1981, with a significant advantage over the Ka-25PL in that it possesses a hover coupler allowing the dunking sonar to be used at night and in adverse weather conditions. Curiously, given the fact that it has a substantial payload capability, the type is generally operated in tactically inefficient pairs, one helicopter acquiring and tracking the target submarine that is then attacked by the weapons carried by the partner helicopter. The Ka-28 'Helix-A' is the export version with a powerplant of two 2,173hp (1,620kW) TV3-117BK turboshafts, and presumably delivered with a different (probably lower) avionics standard.

The Ka-29TB 'Helix-B' is the dedicated Naval Infantry assault transport with accommodation for 16 fully-equipped troops and, perhaps more importantly, the ability to deliver precision-guided weapons in support of amphibious landings. The type has substantial armour protection for the

Helicopter Survivability

THE importance and cost of helicopter use over the battlefield are so great that in recent years considerable efforts have been made to enhance the ability of such machines not only to survive but also to retain an operational capability even in the course of sustained operations over the modern high-intensity battlefield. The approach to this capability has been undertaken along several lanes including the creation of an airframe (especially the main rotor and critical parts of the fuselage) with the basic strength and structural redundancy to absorb ground fire up to the destructive capability of 23mm cannon without suffering a major structural failure, the adoption of a measure of redundancy in key elements of the dynamic system, the introduction of armour protection for the crew and vital elements of the powerplant and fuel systems, the design and incorporation of seats and a fuel system that is 'crash-resistant' in that the seats attenuate the force of any high-speed impact with the ground and the fuel system resists any tendency to rupture in the same eventuality, and the use of equipment items to mitigate external threats. These last now include shrouds in the engine inlets to reduce the chance of metal fragment ingestion, a shrouded exhaust system to reduce the thermal signature of this part of the airframe and thereby reduce the target for missiles with infra-red guidance, an infra-red jammer and/or ejectable thermal flares that help to defeat the guidance of missiles with infra-red guidance, a laser warning system to alert the crew to the 'illumination' of their helicopter by a laser designation system, and a radar warning receiver and chaff launcher system to warn of the radar 'illumination' of the helicopter and then help to defeat the guidance package of any missile with radar guidance.

cockpit and engine bay, and the embarked troops are carried in a hold 14ft 10in (4.52m) long, 4ft 3in (1.30m) wide and 4ft 4in (1.32m) high. Rapid egress is facilitated by the provision on the port side of the fuselage, behind the main landing gear unit, of a door horizontally divided into upward- and downward-opening sections. The helicopter's fixed armament comprises one 0.3in (7.62mm) rotary four-barrel machine gun on a flexible mounting behind the downward-articulated door on the starboard side of the nose, and one optional 30mm 2A42 cannon on a fixed mounting on the port side of the fuselage; the disposable armament is carried on four hardpoints under braced outriggers, and comprises four-round launchers for AT-6 'Spiral' anti-tank missiles, or UV-32-57 multiple launchers each carrying thirty-two 2.17in (55mm) S-5 unguided rockets, or two pods each carrying two 23mm GSh-23L two-barrel cannon, or two 1,102lb (500kg) incendiary bombs. This variant's standard electronics include optronic and missile-guidance pods under the nose, an ESM system with its antenna above the rear part of the engine bay forward of the IR jammer, and an RWR.

Originally known as the Ka-29RLD 'Helix-B', the Ka-31 is the carrierborne AEW member of the family with surveillance radar whose antenna hinges down from the horizontal position under the fuselage to the vertical position before it starts to rotate in its search for fighter-sized echoes out to a maximum range of 93 miles (150km). The Ka-31 also has two equipment panniers on the starboard side of the cabin, an extended tail cone probably accommodating the antenna for an ESM/ECM system, a crew of two, and an endurance of 2 hours 30 minutes at an altitude of 11,480ft (3,500m). The NATO reporting name 'Helix-C' has been given to the Ka-32 civil helicopter.

The Ka-32S 'Helix-C' is the general-purpose member of the Ka-27 series that can be used in roles as diverse as SAR, planeguard and under-way replenishment of warships at sea. Although based on the 'Helix-A', the type has the two external fuel tanks of the 'Helix-C' and is fitted with a rescue hoist.

Reverting once more to the Western world, the S-61 was supported and then supplanted in its land-based military role by the 1961 Boeing Vertol CH-47 Chinook medium-lift helicopter, which is one of history's truly classic helicopters and was particularly valuable in Vietnam for moving vehicles and artillery to the weight of 12,000lb (5,443kg) into every combat area. The Chinook remains in production in the mid-1990s, the latest helicopters of this important type having greatly increased power and much-enhanced avionics.

The origins of the type can be traced back to the later years of the 1950s, when the US Army decided to procure a new helicopter for the battlefield mobility role, and initially ordered 10 examples of the Vertol Model 107 tandem-rotor design for evaluation under the designation YHC-1A. It was already becoming clear that the Model 107 was too small and lacking in power to meet the US Army's requirement, so the YHC-1A order was curtailed to just three helicopters as the service evaluated design submissions from

five manufacturers to meet a requirement that included all-weather capability and a payload including 40 fully equipped troops or freight varying between 4,000lb (1,814kg) carried internally or 16,000lb (7,257kg) carried externally. Other elements of the requirement were straight-in loading and unloading via a power-operated rear ramp/door arrangement, and provision for the hold to be configured for the transport of litters when the helicopter was used in the casevac role.

Vertol accordingly developed the Model 114 as an enlarged version of the Model 107 concept with considerably greater power from two turboshafts pod-mounted above and outside the rear fuselage and in line with the rear rotor pylon. Other obvious changes included fixed quadricycle landing gear and fuel tankage in the long side panniers that extended over three-quarters of the fuselage length and were sealed to provide additional waterborne buoyancy and stability.

The US Army ordered five examples of the Model 114 for evaluation under the designation YHC-1B (soon altered to YCH-47A). The first of these helicopters flew in September 1961 with a powerplant of two 2,200hp (1,641kW) Lycoming T55-L-5 turboshafts, and the CH-47A production model, of which 349 were built, entered service from December 1962 with a powerplant of two T55-L-5 turboshafts that were supplanted later in the production run by 2,650hp (1,976kW) T55-L-7 turboshafts.

Proved by a CH-47A conversion that first flew in October 1966, the CH-47B was an upgraded model with a powerplant of two 2,850hp (2,125kW)

Right: The Aérospatiale (now Eurocopter France) SA. 330 Puma in flight. This baseline model of the Puma, Super Puma and Cougar series was designed in the early 1960s and is still in widespread service. The tactical transport models carry a flightcrew of up to three, and a payload of 20 troops, or six litters and six seated casualties, or 6,614lb (3,000kg) of freight in the cabin or 7,055lb (3,200kg) of freight as a slung load.

Left: Infantrymen disembark from an Aérospatiale (now Eurocopter France) SA. 330 Puma of the French forces in a display of typical air-mobility tactics for the modern battlefield.

T55-L-7C turboshafts, modified rotor blades, and a number of detail improvements. The variant was delivered from May 1967, and production amounted to 108 helicopters.

The final new-build model of the Chinook was the much-improved CH-47C variant with 3,750hp (2,796kW) T55-L-11A turboshafts, an uprated transmission and greater internal fuel capacity. The first example flew in October 1967 for a service debut early in 1968, and production amounted to 270 helicopters. All surviving CH-47As and CH-47Bs were later upgraded to this same improved standard and, from the late 1970s, 182 survivors have been fitted with glassfibre rotor blades.

The CH-47D's extensively updated standard incorporates 13 major improvements such as more powerful engines, further strengthened transmission, rotor blades of composite construction, crash-resistant features, and more advanced avionics. The type has a three-point external attachment system to cater for heavy loads, and the first of a planned 472 older helicopters upgraded to this standard was redelivered in May 1982. The CH-47D's hold has a length of 30ft 6in (9.30m), a mean width of 7ft 6in (2.29m) increasing to 8ft 3in (2.51m) at floor level, and a height of 6ft 6in (1.98m), and this payload volume is accessed by a hydraulically powered rear ramp/door that can be left completely or partially open in flight, or even removed entirely to permit the loading of outsize freight items.

Pending deliveries of the MH-47E, 32 CH-47Ds have been revised as CH-47D Special Operations Aircraft with an inflight-refuelling probe some 24ft 0in (8.53m) long and located on the starboard side of the forward fuselage, an imaging FLIR system, weather radar, improved communication and navigation equipment, a navigator/commander station, and provision for two 0.3in (7.62mm) pintle-mounted machine guns.

CH-47D International Chinook is the basic designation of military Chinooks built by Boeing and licensed as the Model 414 for the export market with a triple external hook system for a load of 26,000lb (11,793kg) on the central unit, or 17,000lb (7,711kg) on the forward or rear units, or 23,000lb (10,433kg) on the forward and rear units combined. The type differs from the baseline CH-47D in its alternative powerplant of two T55-L-714 turboshafts each rated at 5,069hp (3,780kW) for take-off and 4,168hp (3,108kW) for continuous running, and driving a transmission rated at 7,500hp (5,593kW) on two engines and 4,600hp (3,430kW) on one engine. Other differences include a longer nose allowing the installation of weather radar.

The MH-47E is the US Special Forces version of the CH-47D under development from the later 1980s for service from 1994. Production of 51 such helicopters is schemed within the CH-47D total of 472 machines. The type was planned to carry a maximum of 44 troops, and its typical mission of 5 hours 30 minutes involves delivering 36 troops under adverse day/night conditions over a radius of 345 miles (560km) in temperate operating conditions, or 30 troops over the same radius under hot-and-high operating conditions.

The MH-47E has the lengthened fuselage of the CH-47D International Chinook with the forward wheels moved 3ft 4in (1.02m) closer to the nose to allow the use of longer side pannier tanks that increase fuel capacity in conjunction with two floor tanks, an inflight-refuelling capability via the retractable probe on the starboard side of the forward fuselage, and an advanced electronic suite based on two digital databuses for the integration of items such as terrain-avoidance/following, ground mapping and air-to-surface ranging radar, an inertial navigation system (INS) with inputs from the Doppler navigation and GPS receiver and terrain-referenced positioning navigation systems, digital moving map display, a 'glass' cockpit with four head-down displays compatible with night vision goggles, an FLIR sensor in

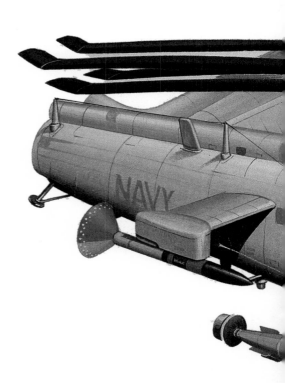

a chin turret, and a defensive subsystem incorporating a laser warning system, radar warning receiver, missile warning system, pulse radar jammer, continuous-wave radar jammer, and chaff/flare dispensers.

The type carries armament in the form of two 0.5in (12.7mm) Browning M2 heavy machine guns mounted in the port forward and starboard aft windows for the suppression of defensive fire, and can also carry defensive FIM-92 Stinger short-range air-to-air missiles (AAMs) aimed via the FLIR system.

The Chinook has also been built under licence in Italy and Japan as the Meridionali (Boeing) CH-47C and Kawasaki (Boeing) CH-47J.

The smaller counterpart of the CH-47, and indeed the type from which it was developed in conceptual terms, is the Boeing Vertol CH-46 Sea Knight. This type's origins can be discerned in the 1956 decision by Vertol, shortly after its creation, to design a medium helicopter optimised for civil use but possessing the features that would allow its evolution into a military type should such a demand materialise. The design team decided on a powerplant of two turboshaft engines as, despite its technical infancy, this type of engine offered an attractive combination of small installation volume, high power-to-weight ratio, low vibration and, in a twin-engined powerplant arrangement, good reliability and safety factors. The design team also opted for a twin-rotor design of the pattern established in the USA by Piasecki, for this avoided the technical demands associated with a single and inevitably much larger main rotor, and also reduced the need for careful weight

The Sikorsky S-70B is the naval version of the land-based S-70A series in service with the US Army as the H-60 Black Hawk in a number of missions for a variety of roles. The S-70B serves with the US Navy (as well as a number of other services) as the SH-60 Seahawk with features such as a folding tail and folding main rotor blades. The two main variants are the SH-60B Seahawk intended for the light airborne multi-purpose system Mk III (LAMPS III) role on destroyers and therefore fitted with search radar, magnetic-anomaly detection equipment, an electronic support measures system, sonobuoys used in association with an advanced acoustic data-processing system, and a data-link system, and the SH-60F Ocean Hawk carried by aircraft carriers for the battle group protection role with dunking sonar. Illustrated here is the SH-60B variant.

The LAMPS Concept

IN 1967 the Israeli destroyer *Eilat* was sunk by a Soviet-supplied SS-N-2 'Styx' anti-ship missile fired by an Egyptian fast attack craft lying at anchor in Alexandria harbour, and this first operational success by a guided missile against a warship exerted considerable influence on naval thinking in the West, which had up to that time considered the anti-ship missile as a limited threat. It was now clear that the anti-ship missile was a major threat, and this was all the more dangerous as the USSR was clearly the world leader in the design and development of such weapons in the surface- as well as air-launched roles. Considerable effort was therefore expended in creating Western weapons of comparable lethality, resulting in the Aérospatiale Exocet and McDonnell Douglas Harpoon series to complement a few conceptually older weapons, and also in the rapid development of methods of defeating the anti-ship missile of the sea-skimming type that was deemed the greater threat than a missile flying at higher altitude. The defeat of such missiles was considered possible with fire from anti-aircraft guns, especially after the introduction of close-in weapon system mountings such as the Phalanx with its radar-controlled 20mm Vulcan six-barrel rotary cannon, but only if sufficient warning could be provided of the missile's arrival. This was the spur for the creation of the Light Airborne Multi-Purpose System helicopter that could be carried by smaller warships for its full range of operational requirements. The LAMPS helicopter had therefore to retain its current anti-submarine capability with dunking sonar and/or sonobuoys together with homing torpedoes, in combination with the new task of searching for, finding and reporting incoming anti-ship missiles. The task of searching for such missiles was entrusted to a combination of an active radar and a passive electronic support measures system, the former sending out its own radar pulses and the latter detecting the radar pulses of the missile radar guidance, and the timely relay of information about missile position, course and speed was made possible by the incorporation of a data-link system feeding information straight into the central computer of the parent ship's combat information centre, which then alerted and controlled the appropriate weapon in the interception and destruction of the incoming missile. The LAMPS I helicopter is the Kaman SH-2 Seasprite, now in the last stages of replacement on larger ships by the LAMPS III helicopter, namely the Sikorsky SH-60B Seahawk.

distribution of the payload to avoid centre of gravity problems. The engines were located above and behind the hold in the angles between the rear pylon and upper rear fuselage, and the transmission system ensured that, in the event of one engine failing, the other drove both rotors, which were carefully synchronised to avoid the possibility of blade tip clash in the area above the fuselage where the two rotors intermeshed.

The new design was designated Model 107, and in structural terms was based on a rectangular-section fuselage comprising the cockpit at the front, the hold in the centre, and a ramp/door arrangement in the lower side of the upswept tail unit. The landing gear was of the fixed tricycle type, with the main units carried under the large rear sponsons that also accommodated the fuel tanks, and the design of the fuselage as a compartmented and sealed unit opened the possibility of waterborne operation.

The Model 107 prototype first flew in April 1958, and in July the US Army ordered 10 (later reduced to three) examples for evaluation under the designation YHC-1A. The first of these helicopters flew in August 1959 with a powerplant of two 860hp (641kW) Lycoming T53 turboshafts, but by this time the US Army had decided that it needed a larger type to satisfy its battlefield mobility requirement, and no production order was placed.

Vertol had already reached the conclusion that the type lacked the performance and payload necessary to attract potential customers, and revised the third YHC-1A with larger-diameter rotors driven by two 1,050hp (783kW) General Electric T58-GE-6 turboshafts. In this form, the helicopter was the Model 107-II prototype that first flew in October 1960. The US Marine Corps had already seen the type as the basis of the assault helicopter it required as successor to its Sikorsky HUS-1 Seahorse, and Vertol developed the Model 107-II design as the militarised Model 107M which the US Marine Corps ordered as the HRB-1.

By March 1960, Vertol had become a division of the Boeing Company, and it was as a Boeing Vertol type that the first of these 164 helicopters flew in October 1962, by which time the designation had been altered to CH-46A within the new tri-service designation system. The type entered service from June 1964 with a powerplant of two 1,250hp (932kW) T58-GE-8B turboshafts for the carriage of a payload that could comprise 25 troops, or 15 litters plus two attendants, or 4,000lb (1,814kg) of freight carried over a range of 115 miles (185km) in a hold 24ft 2in (7.37m) long, 6ft 0in (1.83m) wide and 6ft 0in (1.83m) high, and accessed by the hydraulically operated rear ramp/door openable in flight and during water operations.

The HH-46A variant was developed as a base rescue model for the US Navy, and at least 23 were produced as CH-46A conversions with a rescue hoist and other specialised equipment. The RH-46A designation was applied to a few CH-46As converted for use by the US Navy in minesweeping, but the type lacked the power for this particularly exacting role.

The UH-46A was the US Navy's utility counterpart of the US Marine Corps' CH-46A helicopter, and 14 such helicopters were delivered from July 1964 for the primary task of vertical replenishment of under-way task groups and the secondary tasks of personnel transfer and SAR.

The CH-46D model was developed as an upgraded version of the CH-46A, with 1,400hp (1,044kW) T58-GE-10 turboshafts to drive improved rotors featuring cambered blades for greater lift. The type's considerably enhanced lifting power is evidenced by its ability to carry a maximum slung load of 10,000lb (4,536kg). Production amounted to 266 helicopters, and another 12 were produced as conversions from earlier helicopters.

The HH-46D is the US Navy's dedicated SAR version of the CH-46D, of which some 38 were delivered as conversions, while the UH-46D is the US

Navy's vertical replenishment counterpart of the CH-46D and was built to the extent of 10 helicopters supplemented by at least five CH-46As and UH-46As converted to this standard, which includes a powerplant of two 1,400hp (1,044kW) T58-GE-10 turboshafts.

The CH-46E is the standard to which 273 CH-46As, CH-46Ds and CH-46Fs have been upgraded with T58-GE-16 turboshafts, crash-attenuating crew seats, a crash-resistant fuel system, and glassfibre rotor blades. Further improvement was under way in the early 1990s to enhance range in a model unofficially called the CH-46E Bullfrog, featuring larger sponsons for a virtual doubling of the fuel capacity.

The last new-build model was the CH-46F, which was basically an improved CH-46D with updated avionics and equipment. Production amounted to 174 helicopters delivered between July 1968 and February 1971, and many have been revised to CH-46E standard. Five of the helicopters were completed as VIP transports with the designation VH-46F. A small number of export sales were made, and the licence-production rights (later increased to full rights) were sold to Kawasaki, which has produced the type as the Kawasaki KV-107.

In 1962 the Americans finally produced a proper heavy-lift helicopter in the Sikorsky S-64, which bears a close resemblance to the Soviet Mi-10 and entered service as the CH-54 Tarhe. This also proved useful in Vietnam, where it was tested to the limits of its structural strength and versatility. The S-64, for example, was used for naval minesweeping and even to lift light naval vessels.

The origins of the CH-54 can be found in 1958, when Sikorsky began work on its first flying crane helicopter, the S-60, to meet a West German requirement. The S-60 was a radical development of the S-56 that had entered service with the US Marine Corps and US Army (HR2S and H-37 Mojave respectively). The S-60 prototype first flew in March 1959 and, before its loss in a crash in 1961, demonstrated such capabilities that Sikorsky pressed ahead with the design of the larger S-64 that promised still greater capabilities. The type made its initial flight during May 1964 in the form of the first of three S-64A prototypes. The new helicopter was based on a long structural boom that supported, from front to rear, the cabin pod with fixed nosewheel unit, the side-by-side turboshaft engines, the transmission system and six-blade main rotor, the anhedraled outriggers that supported the landing gear's two fixed main units, and the tail pylon complete with four-blade anti-torque rotor.

The most impressive feature of the design was its combination of great ground clearance and a wheel track of 19ft 9in (6.02m), the latter allowing the helicopter to taxi over large loads for attachment to the cargo hook, which was rated at 20,000lb (9,072kg).

In June 1963 the US Army ordered six YCH-54A prototype and service test helicopters with a powerplant of two T73-P-1 turboshafts, and the first of these was delivered in 1964 for trials into the feasibility of using the flying crane helicopter for a host of applications including enhanced battlefield mobility. The YCH-54As were flown operationally in the Vietnam War and demonstrated a useful heavy-lift capability, including the ability to carry the specially designed Universal Pod that could accommodate 67 troops, or 48

Designed by Aérospatiale (now Eurocopter France) with the aid of Sikorsky, the SA. 321 Super Frelon (hornet) had a boat hull and float-type stabilizing sponsons for full amphibious capability, and is now used mainly for the protection of the French nuclear submarine base at Brest in north-west France, where the type uses its dunking sonar and/or search radar to detect underwater intruders that would then be attacked with depth charges or homing torpedoes. This SA. 321G variant has a flightcrew of two and a mission crew of three, the latter replaceable by 27 troops or 11,023lb (5,000kg) of freight for the alternative transport role, and its other details include a powerplant of three 1,609hp (1,200kW) Turbomeca Turmo III turboshafts, main rotor diameter of 62ft 0in (18.90m), fuselage length of 63ft 7.75in (19.40m), height of 22ft 2.1in (6.76m), maximum take-off weight of 28,660lb (13,000kg), maximum speed of 154mph (248km/h) at sea level, service ceiling of 10,170ft (3,100m) and range of 633 miles (1,020km) with a 7,716lb (3,500kg) payload.

litters, or a field hospital, or 22,890lb (10,383kg) of freight. The US Army then ordered 54 examples of the CH-54A production model that played an important part in the later stages of the Vietnam War for the recovery of downed aircraft and the movement of heavy equipment such as bulldozers.

The CH-54B is an improved version of the CH-54A, most readily identifiable by the twin wheels on its main landing gear units. The type also has a strengthened structure, greater power, higher-lift rotor blades and, as a retrofit on some helicopters, provision for two external tanks. The US Army ordered 37 of this version, which differs from the CH-54A in details such as its maximum payload of 25,000lb (11,340kg) and powerplant of two 4,800hp (3,579kW) T73-P-700 (JFTD12A-5A) turboshafts.

France's only heavy-lift helicopter, the Aérospatiale SA.321 Super Frelon, was adopted by several nations: the Israelis made good use of the type as a commando carrier, but the Super Frelon is very versatile and is currently operated by the French as a land-based heavy anti-submarine helicopter.

Developed as the production version of the SA.3210 prototype that flew in December 1962 as an evolution of the SA.3200 Frelon, the Super Frelon was designed with the aid of Sikorsky in the evolution of the dynamic system (powerplant, transmission and rotors). As a result, the type has a number of Sikorsky features reminiscent of the American company's S-61 (SH-3 Sea King), such as its watertight hull with a boat bottom, the tricycle landing gear with twin wheels on each unit, and the Sikorsky-designed dynamic system based on a six-blade main rotor and a five-blade tail rotor driven by three rather than two turboshafts, located as a side-by-side pair forward of the combining gearbox and the third engine to the rear of the gearbox.

The first prototype was representative of the planned assault transport version, and used a powerplant of three 1,250hp (932kW) Turbomeca Turmo IIIC2 turboshafts. The second prototype first flew in May 1963 and was representative of the naval version with stabilising sponsons on the main landing gear support structures to provide a genuine waterborne capability. The second prototype impressed the French naval air arm, which ordered three of the four pre-production prototypes with more powerful engines.

The first of the pre-production prototypes flew in November 1965, and their overall success led Sud-Aviation to expect a major commercial success for the Super Frelon in the civil as well as military markets. This success was not to be achieved, however, for few civil orders were placed and even the military orders were disappointingly low. The SA.321A land-based transport, SA.321B land-based troop transport, SA.321C land-based civil transport, SA.321D maritime ASW, and SA.321E maritime transport models were not built, and only one example of the SA.321F civil transport was produced, with a powerplant of three Turmo IIIC3 turboshafts.

The SA.321G naval demonstrator was powered by three Turmo IIIC6 turboshafts and was fitted with a folding main rotor and a hinged tail boom to reduce overall length for easier shipborne stowage. This paved the way for the French naval air arm's production version, which was delivered in the form of five SA.321Ga radarless transports with a powerplant of three Turmo IIIC3 turboshafts, and 19 SA.321Gb multi-role helicopters. Both models have a cabin 22ft 11.5in (11.00m) long, 6ft 2.75in (1.90m) wide and 6ft 0in (1.83m) high, and this is accessed by a starboard-side sliding door as well as a hydraulically powered ramp/door arrangement that allows straight in/out loading and unloading, and can be opened in flight for the dispatch of parachute-equipped men and loads.

The SA.321Gb helicopters were delivered with nose radar and provision for use in the anti-submarine role, most notably the protection of the sea approaches to the harbour of Brest, base for the French navy's nuclear-powered submarine force. The first 12 helicopters form a distinct subvariant with Sylphe nose-mounted radar and a powerplant of three Turmo IIIC3 turboshafts, while the last seven constitute a slightly different subvariant with Sylphe nose radar that was often replaced by ORB 31D radar and a powerplant of three Turmo IIIC7 turboshafts for an increased maximum take-off weight.

Export derivatives of the SA.321G were the SA.321GM for Libya (six helicopters delivered in 1980 and 1981 with a powerplant of three Turmo IIIC7 turboshafts, ORB 31WAS radar and dunking sonar), and the SA.321GV for Iraq (16 helicopters delivered between 1976 and 1981 in two batches with ORB 31D radar).

The SA.321Ja is the float-equipped transport and anti-submarine version sold to China and Zaire. The 16 helicopters for China were delivered between 1975 and 1977 with ORB 32AS radar and a powerplant of three 1,549hp (1,155kW) Turmo IIIC6 turboshafts. The single helicopter for Zaire was delivered as a presidential transport without radar.

The SA.321K is a simplified land-based transport helicopter that was developed as the SA.321H without stabilising floats. The type was placed in production in two differently designated variants for Israel and South Africa. The variant for Israel was the SA.321K, which was built in two subvariants as the SA.321Ka and SA.321Kb totalling 14 helicopters including replacements for two machines that crashed before delivery. The original order covered five SA.321Ka and seven SA.321Kb helicopters, and these were delivered from 1967 with a powerplant of three 1,475hp (1,100kW) Turmo IIIE3 turboshafts for the carriage of a payload that could comprise 30 troops, or 15 litters, or a freight load of 8,818 or 11,023lb (4,000 or 5,000kg) carried internally or externally. The helicopters were later revised with a powerplant of three 1,895hp (1,413kW) General Electric T58-GE-16 turboshafts. The variant for South Africa was the SA.321L, of which 16 were delivered between 1967 and 1969, without floats or radar but with a powerplant of three 1,569hp (1,170kW) turboshafts.

The SA.321M was the transport version for Libya, which received eight such helicopters in 1971 and 1972, without radar but with floats and a powerplant of three 1,569hp (1,170kW) turboshafts.

The influence of Sikorsky on the Aérospatiale (now Eurocopter France) SA. 321 Super Frelon is evident in the design of the hull/float combination and of the dynamic system with its three engines powering a drive train that turns a six-blade main rotor and five-blade tail rotor.

The Gunship Helicopter

THE Bell Model 209 HueyCobra of 1965 was the first helicopter gunship to enter production and service. The type's advent heralded the split of helicopter design into more specialised types. Although it suffered heavy losses in Vietnam, the HueyCobra soon proved itself a valuable weapon incorporating considerable development potential. With its remotely controlled chin turret aimed by the co-pilot/gunner and its long, narrow fuselage, it showed clearly that armed helicopters could be used as close-support types for the accurate delivery of machine gun, cannon and grenade fire as well as unguided rockets and, in later variants, guided missiles such as the Hughes BGM-71 TOW wire-guided anti-tank missile; the HueyCobra can also carry a cannon pack. Although other helicopters had been fitted with armament (principally machine guns firing from the side doors and a number of different light ASM types) for use in the close-support role, it was with the HueyCobra that the concept came to maturity.

First flown in September 1965 as the private-venture Model 209 with a powerplant of one 1,100hp (820kW) Lycoming T53-L-11 turboshaft, the AH-1G HueyCobra evolved from the company's D-255 Iroquois Warrior design concept. This new type was required to meet an urgent demand by the US Army in the Vietnam War for a helicopter gunship able to escort its troop-carrying Bell UH-1 Iroquois helicopters, and to provide fire support for the troops landed from these tactical transport machines.

The Iroquois Warrior concept had been based on the D-245 design with small swept auxiliary wings, and resembled a hybrid rotary- and fixed-wing aeroplane in its combination of a slender fuselage (of small cross-section and very narrow profile) with vertically stepped tandem cockpits (which located the co-pilot/gunner below and forward of the pilot), retractable skid landing gear, stub wings, provision for extensive armament (including a streamlined cannon installation under the fuselage) and the dynamic system of the Model 204. The US Army examined the Iroquois Warrior mock-up in June 1962, but in August of the same year the Howze Board recommended the establishment of Air Cavalry Combat Brigades, and Bell decided to evolve an attack helicopter tailored specifically to the need of the new type of unit.

A first step was the conversion of a Model 47 into the Model 207 Sioux Scout prototype. This handled well and could carry a useful armament load, but Bell rightly appreciated that higher performance and maximum compatibility with current turbine-engined helicopters were essential factors, and therefore opted to develop a gunship variant of the Model 204. This was the D-262, in essence a scaled-down version of the D-255 for competition with Lockheed and Sikorsky designs in the advanced aerial fire-support system (AAFSS) competition.

Much to Bell's disappointment, the D-262 was the first casualty of the competition, which was won by the Lockheed design that was ordered in the form of 10 YAH-56A Cheyenne prototype and service test helicopters. The AAFSS requirement had called for a highly sophisticated helicopter, and the

The Bell AH-1 HueyCobra was developed with commendable speed as the Model 209 with the dynamic system of the UH-1C Iroquois or 'Huey' tactical transport helicopter married to a new and extremely slender fuselage carrying the crew of two, in vertically staggered seating that provided optimum fields of vision, and an armament scheme that was based on a trainable undernose turret carrying two 0.3in (7.62mm) Minigun machine guns, or two 40mm grenade launchers or one example of each weapon type, and rockets and/or gun pods on the four hardpoints under the stub wing.

order for 375 production examples of the Cheyenne was finally cancelled because of protracted development and financial problems.

Bell had realised that the development phase of the AAFSS programme would be so protracted that an interim type would be needed, and in December 1964 decided to proceed with the private-venture development of such a type as the Model 209 Cobra on the basis of the D-262. The company determined that the prototype should be completed in no more than one year and at a cost not exceeding $1 million; in the event, Bell bettered the time but missed the cost limit by a mere $40,000.

Work started in March 1965, and key elements in the design were a fuselage modelled on that of the D-262 with its width limited to 3ft 2in (0.97m), a powerplant of one 1,100hp (820kW) T53-L-11 turboshaft driving a UH-1C transmission system and a Model 540 rotor with blades of 2ft 3in (0.686m) chord, the traditional stabilizer bar replaced by a stability control augmentation system, the boom and tail unit (complete with anti-torque

Bell validated the concept of the helicopter gunship in its Model 208 Sioux Scout, which was a conversion from H-13 (Model 47) standard with the main features desired for a helicopter gunship. The type was too small and too poorly powered for any real consideration as a production type.

One of the most advanced helicopter gunships yet flown, the Lockheed AH-56 Cheyenne was designed to satisfy the US Army's extremely ambitious advanced aerial fire-support system (AAFSS) requirement, and was powered by two turboshafts, most of whose power was transferred to the large pusher propeller at the tail once the helicopter had translated into forward flight with much of its weight supported by the comparatively large stub wing. The Cheyenne was troubled by major development problems, however, and was cancelled in August 1972.

rotor but with a longer-span tailplane) of the UH-1C, small but unswept stub wings and, after considerable discussion, retractable twin-skid landing gear. The armament comprised a fixed element of one Emerson Electric chin turret carrying one 0.3in (7.62mm) General Electric GAU-2B/A Minigun rotary six-barrel machine gun with 4,000 rounds of ammunition, and a disposable element in the form of stores was carried on four hardpoints under the stub wings.

Construction of the prototype was well advanced when the US Army called for an interim gunship helicopter for service in South Vietnam within 24 months. Bell offered its Model 209 in August 1965, and other submissions were the Boeing Vertol H-47 Chinook, Kaman Tomahawk (H-2 Seasprite derivative with stub wings and a pair of twin-gun barbettes side-by-side under the nose), Piasecki Pathfinder and Sikorsky S-61.

The Model 209 prototype first flew in September 1965, three weeks ahead of Bell's own schedule. After a fairly intensive development effort, the Model 209 was evaluated against the H-2 and the S-61, and was declared winner of the competition in March 1966. The US Army's procurement of the resulting AH-1 began with just two pre-production helicopters based on the Model 209 but modified with fixed landing gear, a larger chin turret, and a stronger stub wing to cater for the heavier disposable loads anticipated by the operating service. The first of these two machines flew in October 1966, and

When the AAFSS requirement was superseded by the less demanding Advanced Attack Helicopter requirement, the winning contender was the Hughes Model 77 that was ordered as the AH-64A Apache and later became a McDonnell Douglas type after the latter's purchase of the Hughes helicopter operation. The Apache is the most advanced battlefield attack helicopter currently in large-scale service, and the AH-64A initial production model is notable for its somewhat angular but powerful appearance, excellent defensive features, powerful offensive armament, and highly capable flight and fire-control electronics. The armament is based on a 30mm trainable cannon under the fuselage and up to 3,880lb (1,760kg) of weapons including no fewer than 16 AGM-114 Hellfire anti-tank missiles carried on four hardpoints under the stub wings, and further capability is being added by the conversion of many surviving AH-64A helicopters to the AH-64D standard with the mast-mounted Longbow fire-control system that allows the helicopter to lurk behind cover but still see the target area electronically and control missiles fired into it.

the helicopters were then used in an accelerated development programme to qualify the weapons capability and stability control augmentation system.

The first AH-1G emerged from the production line in May 1967 and deliveries to the US Army began in June of the same year, with a powerplant of one 1,400hp (1,044kW) T53-L-13 turboshaft derated to 1,100hp (820kW), a Model 540 main rotor and, in all but the first helicopters, the anti-torque rotor relocated from the port to the starboard side of the tail pylon.

The turret was initially the Emerson Electric TAT-102A unit carrying a 0.3in (7.62mm) General

The first production version of the Bell AH-1 HueyCobra series was the AH-1G whose details included a powerplant of one 1,400hp (1,044kW) Lycoming T53-L-13 turboshaft derated to 1,100hp (820kW), main rotor diameter of 44ft 0in (13.41m), fuselage length of 44ft 7in (13.59m), height of 13ft 6.25in (4.12m), maximum take-off weight of 9,500lb (4,309kg), maximum speed of 172mph (277km/h) at sea level, service ceiling of 11,400ft (3,475m) and range of 357 miles (574km). Late variants have retained the same basic layout with a considerably uprated powerplant whose additional power is used not for performance enhancement but rather for the ability to operate effectively with additional offensive and defensive equipment, the former now including heavyweight wire-guided anti-tank missiles.

Electric M134 Minigun rotary six-barrel machine gun with 8,000 rounds of ammunition, although this was later supplanted by the TAT-141 turret (part of the Emerson Electric M28 weapon system) carrying two Miniguns with 4,000 rounds per gun, or two 40mm Hughes (later McDonnell Douglas Helicopters) M129 grenade launchers with 300 rounds per weapon, or one example of each weapon type. Structural provision was also made for the TAT-141 to be replaced by the General Electric Universal Turret System carrying one 20mm General Electric M197 rotary three-barrel cannon. The chin turret was usually fired by the co-pilot/gunner using the hand-held pantograph M73 reflex sight to which the turret was slaved, and the disposable armament was usually controlled by the pilot, although either crew member could control the whole armament if necessary. The four hardpoints under the stub wing could lift up to 2,200lb (998kg) of ordnance such as four M159 multiple launchers each carrying nineteen 2.75in (70mm) unguided rockets, or four M157 multiple launchers each carrying seven 2.75in unguided rockets, or two General Electric M18 or M18E1 0.3in Minigun pods, or one General Electric M35 armament system with one 20mm General Electric M195 Vulcan rotary six-barrel cannon with 1,000 rounds; this last item was carried on the port inner hardpoint.

The HueyCobra's battlefield tasking was reflected in the provision of an armoured windscreen and Norton Company NOROC armour protection for the crew and vital areas such as the engine compressor.

The production total for the AH-1G was soon raised to 838 helicopters, and the first machines were deployed to South Vietnam by the autumn of 1967, only a few weeks after the type's service debut. The AH-1G proved very useful for the close-support and attack roles in the Vietnamese fighting, a fact recognised in the placement of additional contracts that raised the production total to an eventual 1,126 helicopters of which the last was delivered in February 1973, and some of these machines were later transferred to US allies as they became surplus to US Army requirements.

Some 38 of the helicopters were transferred in February 1969 to the US Marine Corps, whose commitment in the northern part of South Vietnam urgently required the support of fast and agile armed helicopters. A few other examples were converted into TH-1G dual-control trainers for the conversion of AH-1 pilots.

Developed in the early 1970s in the Improved Cobra Armament Program

(ICAP), the following AH-1Q was an interim anti-tank helicopter produced to fill the operational gap left by the failure of the AH-56. This gap lay in the US Army's ability to supplement the efforts of its ground forces with air-delivered weapons in the defeat of any tank-spearheaded Warsaw Pact invasion of Western Europe. The US Army therefore decided to re-equip its existing AH-1G force with BGM-71 TOW heavyweight anti-tank missiles and to procure additional helicopters of the same basic type.

The US Army placed its ICAP contract in March 1972, this specifying the conversion of eight AH-1Gs to YAH-1Q standard with TOW missiles and the Sperry-Univac helmet-directed fire-control subsystem (HDFCS). The first conversion was delivered in February 1973, and successful trials paved the way for the January 1974 contract ordering an initial 101 'production' conversions, supplemented in December 1974 by a contract for another 189 conversions to the same standard.

In the event, only 92 such conversions were completed with provision for eight TOW anti-tank missiles (four under each outer underwing hardpoint) controlled with the aid of a Hughes M65 sight system for the gunner in the front seat, who also had the HDFCS. The other 198 helicopters did not receive the conversion because the weight and drag of the TOW system seriously degraded manoeuvrability and performance.

As a consequence of the TOW system shortcomings, the US Army contracted with Bell for the Improved Cobra Agility and Maneuverability (ICAM) program involving two prototype conversions. Bell's response to the ICAM requirement was centred on the use of a much-uprated powerplant, a development of the T53-L-13 turboshaft known as the T53-L-703 and rated at 1,800hp (1,342kW), together with a revised transmission and the tail rotor of the Model 212.

The first prototype was the YAH-1R conversion of an AH-1G and the second was the YAH-1S conversion of an AH-1Q with full TOW capability. The two helicopters were evaluated from December 1974, and their performance confirmed the value of the uprated powerplant so emphatically that, in June 1975, the US Army ordered the completion of the AH-1Q programme and the conversion of existing AH-1Qs to this improved standard with the uprated dynamic system (as noted above), as well as fibreglass main rotor blades, a primary offensive armament of eight TOW anti-tank missiles, better defensive capabilities, and improved fire-control subsystems.

The helicopters were initially allocated the designation AH-1S (Mod) HueyCobra, but in 1987 the revised designation AH-1S HueyCobra was decreed. Some 15 of the helicopters were further converted with the designation TH-1S (Mod) Night Stalker for use by the Army National Guard as pilot's night vision system (PNVS) and integrated helmet and display sighting system (IHADSS) trainers for the McDonnell Douglas AH-64A Apache, and in 1987 these helicopters were also redesignated, in this instance to TH-1S Night Stalker.

In 1975 the US Army undertook the Priority Aircraft Subsystem Suitability (PASS) review, to fix ways in which the HueyCobra's capabilities could be extended beyond the limits of the ICAP and ICAM programmes. The review decided that the best course of action was to improve the basic helicopter's capabilities against the new generation of anti-aircraft weapons being developed and introduced by the USSR, through the incorporation of a new cockpit canopy, improved instrumentation, superior ECM equipment, and upgraded armament.

As a result of the review, Bell received orders for 305 (later reduced to 297) HueyCobras in three steadily-improving versions. The first of these was the AH-1S (Prod) HueyCobra with the same dynamic system

McDonnell Douglas AH-64 Apache Electronics

THE two most important groups of sensors carried by the McDonnell Douglas AH-64 Apache anti-tank and battlefield close-support helicopter are the target acquisition and designation system (TADS) and pilot's night vision sensor (PNVS). Northrop and Martin Marietta competed for these complex systems, Martin Marietta winning in April 1982. The two independent systems are both turret-mounted in the extreme nose and feed data to the two members of the crew via the monocle screen carried by the helmet of the integrated helmet and display sighting system (IHADDS). The TADS is based on a nose turret that can be traversed 120° left and right of the centreline and elevated in an arc between -60° and +30°. The turret accommodates daylight and night/all-weather sensors in its port and starboard halves respectively: the daylight sensors comprise a TV camera with wide- and narrow-angle fields of vision, direct-view optics with wide- and narrow-angle fields of vision, a laser spot tracker, and an International Laser Systems laser ranger and designator, while the night/adverse-weather sensor is an FLIR with wide-, medium- and narrow-angle fields of vision. In short, the TADS provides for the optronic, optical or thermal acquisition of targets that can then be laser-ranged and laser-designated to allow manual or automatic tracking for autonomous engagement with the cannon, missiles or rockets. It is worth noting, moreover, that while the TADS is designed primarily for the co-pilot/gunner, it provides back-up night vision capability for the pilot in the event of a failure in the PNVS. This latter is based on an FLIR in a separate turret located above the TADS turret, and this sensor's 20° and 40° fields of vision provide high-resolution thermal imaging for day/night nap-of-the-earth flight profiles under all weather conditions. The co-pilot/gunner is primarily responsible for the armament, which comprises disposable stores carried on the four underwing hardpoints and the 30mm cannon in an underfuselage installation designed to collapse upward between the two crew members in the event of a crash landing. The pilot can override the co-pilot/gunner in use of the weapons, but his principal task is flying the helicopter with the aid of the highly advanced all-weather systems that include the PNVS, Lear Siegler inertial

Continued on page 97

improvements as the AH-1S (Mod) but with a flat-plate canopy for reduced glint, an improved cockpit layout, better instrumentation for nap-of-the-earth operations, the APR-39 RWR, and (from the 67th helicopter) composite-structure rotor blades developed by Kaman. These 100 helicopters were redelivered between the summers of 1977 and 1978, and from 1987 the variant received the revised designation AH-1P HueyCobra.

Sometimes known as the Up-gun AH-1S HueyCobra, the AH-1S (ECAS) second version of the PASS improvement resulted in 98 new-build helicopters, identical to the AH-1S (Prod) machines apart from their provision with the enhanced cobra armament system (ECAS), including an undernose General Electric M79E1 Universal Turret (allowing installation of 20mm or 30mm cannon but used in American helicopters for the 20mm General Electric M197 Vulcan rotary three-barrel cannon) and the M138 underwing stores subsystem for multiple launchers carrying various numbers of unguided rockets. The helicopters were redelivered between September 1978 and October 1979, and in 1987 the variant was redesignated AH-1E HueyCobra.

The third and definitive production version of the HueyCobra resulting from the PASS review was the AH-1S (MC), the letter suffix standing for Modernized Cobra. This has all the features of the AH-1S (Prod) and AH-1S (ECAS) models plus Doppler navigation, an ALQ-144 IR jammer, a secure communications system, and a new fire-control system. This last uses a digital computer linked to a low-airspeed sensor and AAS-32 laser ranger for the solution of ballistic problems, and presents the results on the pilot's Kaiser head-up display (HUD). The initial 99 helicopters of this subvariant were delivered between November 1979 and April 1981, a supplementary batch of 50 helicopters was delivered from April 1981, and finally 337 AH-1Gs were rebuilt to the same standard between November 1979 and June 1982. In 1987 the variant was redesignated AH-1F HueyCobra, and a subvariant of this model is the TAH-1F dual-control trainer of which 41 were delivered as AH-1G conversions with the original designation TAH-1S.

In-service helicopters are being further modernised with the C-NITE system (50 helicopters only) for nocturnal and adverse-weather target detection, acquisition and engagement, the air-to-air Stinger (ATAS) system for FIM-92A Stinger lightweight AAMs, the AVR-2 laser warning system, and the Cobra fleet life extension (C-Flex) upgrade. Israeli helicopters are being fitted with the IAI Cobra Laser Night Attack System, which has a stabilized FLIR and laser ranger and designator to allow the firing of AGM-114A Hellfire missiles out to a range of 11,000yds (10,060m), an advanced mission computer with a moving map display, multi-function displays, a GPS receiver, a four-blade main rotor, a new transmission, and a lengthened tail boom.

The Fuji (Bell) AH-1S is the Japanese licence-built version of the AH-1F, with the 1,800hp (1,342kW) Kawasaki (Lycoming) T53-K-703 turboshaft transmission-limited to 1,290hp (962kW) for take-off and 1,134hp (845kW) for continuous running.

In the autumn of 1967 the US Marine Corps received an initial batch of 38 Bell AH-1G HueyCobra attack helicopters converted with naval avionics, a 20mm cannon in the

The US Marine Corps' counterpart to the US Army's AH-1 HueyCobra, a single-engined type intended only for land-based service, is the AH-1 SeaCobra with a twin-engined powerplant for improved performance and reliability in the type of amphibious operations that are the US Marine Corps *raison d'être*. The original model was the AH-1J SeaCobra, and further variants offering greater offensive and defensive capability have been the AH-1T Improved SeaCobra and the current AH-1W SuperCobra that is illustrated here. The SuperCobra switches from a powerplant of one 2,050hp (1,529kW) Pratt & Whitney Canada T400-WV-402 coupled turboshaft to two General Electric T700-GE-401 turboshafts driving a combining gearbox rated at 3,250hp (2,424kW), and the additional power allows a modest improvement in performance despite the fact that additional offensive and defensive electronics as well as additional weapons have increased the maximum take-off weight from the AH-1T's 14,000lb (6,350kg) to 14,750lb (6,691kg).

chin turret, and a rotor brake. These helicopters provided the marine aviators with an interim close-support capability for their ground forces in the northern part of South Vietnam during the Vietnam War, and also generated useful experience in the operation of attack helicopters. Although generally happy with the AH-1G, the US Marine Corps demanded a more specialised variant with the operational and flight safety advantages of a twin-engined powerplant, as well as a combination of avionics and weapons optimised for the Marine Corps' particular role. Ordered in May 1968, the resulting AH-1J SeaCobra first flew in October 1969, and all 69 production helicopters had been delivered to the Marine Corps by February 1975.

The AH-1J was a derivative of the AH-1G with the powerplant of the Bell UH-1N, namely the 1,800hp (1,342kW) Pratt & Whitney Canada T400-CP-400 coupled turboshaft but flat-rated at 1,250hp (932kW) for take-off and 1,100hp (820kW) for continuous running. Iran procured 202 examples of the AH-1J International derivative with a number of Model 309 KingCobra features and a powerplant of one 1,970hp (1,469kW) T400-WV-402 coupled turboshaft driving a larger-diameter main rotor. The first 140 helicopters were otherwise similar to the standard AH-1J, but the remaining 62 were completed to the more capable AH-1J (TOW) International anti-tank standard, with a revised fire-control system for a primary armament of eight BGM-71 TOW missiles.

In a programme that in many ways paralleled the US Army's development of the AH-1G into more capable variants with an uprated powerplant and a more capable combination of avionics and weapons, the AH-1T Improved SeaCobra variant was developed from the AH-1J but incorporated features of the Model 309 KingCobra and Model 214, including a larger-diameter main rotor as well as a higher-rated power train able to handle the full 1,970hp (1,469kW) delivered by the T400-WV-402 coupled-turboshaft powerplant.

The first of two AH-1J prototype conversions flew in May 1976, and the AH-1T entered service with an armament capability that includes the carriage of BGM-71 TOW or AGM-114 Hellfire anti-tank missiles on its outboard underwing hardpoints. The 57 AH-1Ts were delivered from October 1977, and 39 of the helicopters are being upgraded to AH-1W standard.

Developed as the AH-1T+ to remedy the performance shortfalls of the AH-1T under hot-and-high conditions, the AH-1W SuperCobra model first flew in April 1980 as a converted AH-1T, and entered service in 1987 with considerably improved capabilities resulting from the installation of a much uprated powerplant of two 3,250hp (2,423kW) General Electric T700-GE-401 turboshafts driving a combining gearbox derived from that of the Model 214ST and able to handle a maximum of 3,380hp (2,520kW). The variant's other features include a modified rotor head, a new vibration-suppression system, an upgraded avionics suite, and new subsystems such as a pilot's HUD that is compatible with night vision goggles. In combination with the latest weaponry, this provides the US Marine Corps with a highly advanced close-support and attack helicopter ideally suited to support of beach-head operations from forward airstrips or from assault ships lying just offshore. The primary armament comprises eight BGM-71 TOW or AGM-114 Hellfire anti-tank missiles, supported by a pair of AIM-9L Sidewinder short-range AAMs and AGM-122 SideARM anti-radar missiles for battlefield self-defence. The 84 helicopters were delivered from March 1986. The designation TAH-1W is applied to one dual-control trainer based on the AH-1W.

The AH-1(4B)W Viper is the latest SeaCobra version offered by Bell as a private-venture development of the AH-1W SuperCobra, with the considerably more advanced Model 680 four-blade bearingless main rotor, uprated transmission, an expanded manoeuvring envelope and greater

Continued from page 95

attitude/heading reference system, and Singer-Kearfott Doppler navigation system. This is only one part of the Apache's comprehensive electronics, which also include an RWR, active jammers, chaff/flare dispensers, an IR jammer, and a laser warning system. This core suite, as installed on the AH-64A, is augmented in the AH-64D by the Longbow fire-control system based on a Westinghouse millimetric-wavelength radar with its antenna in a mast-mounted radome above the main rotor. This radar is the primary sensor of the Longbow system (initially designated Airborne Adverse-Weather Weapon System) intended for rapid target-area search, automatic detection and classification of targets, and all-weather fire-and-forget engagement with a revised version of the Hellfire missile, namely the radar-homing Longbow Hellfire that carries, in addition to its semi-active laser seeker modified for improved resistance to optical countermeasures, a combined radio-frequency and IR seeker as well as a warhead optimised for the penetration of modern types of advanced tank protection.

An 'overhead' view of the McDonnell Douglas AH-64A Apache in a nose-down attitude reveals some of this impressive helicopter's most important features including, backward from the nose, the sensor platform for the TADS and IHADSS systems, the lateral panniers carrying most of the electronic equipment, the cockpit with its flat-panel canopy and vertically staggered seats, the stub wing with four hardpoints carrying two rocket-launcher pods outboard and two quadruplets of AGM-114 Hellfire missiles inboard, the four-blade main rotor above the two widely spaced engines, and the tail carrying the four-blade anti-torque rotor.

agility, a digital flight-control system, Doppler navigation, and night-targeting sights. In other respects, the AH-1(4B)W differs from the AH-1W in details such as its cranked stub wing with six hardpoints including overwing launchers for two AGM-122 SideARM anti-radar missiles, a total weapon load of 3,184lb (1,444kg) including 750 rounds of 20mm cannon ammunition and two chaff/flare dispensers, and greater internal fuel capacity.

The Hughes OH-6 Cayuse light utility helicopter, which appeared in 1966, also proved its qualities in Vietnam and has been adopted by several other countries in both its baseline and armed forms. Part of its success derives from its advanced structural design, giving the OH-6 great strength and rigidity at a low weight, and a sleekly streamlined fuselage. The combination of these factors made the OH-6 agile for its size, although not aerobatic. Further development of the type by Hughes and then by McDonnell Douglas after it had bought the company, resulted in the Model 500 intended mainly for the civil market but also developed into the Model 500 Defender series with provision for many types of armament.

The origins of the Kiowa can be found in the realisation by the US Army in the late 1950s that the fixed-wing aeroplane had been rendered obsolete for the battlefield reconnaissance and observation roles. In 1960, therefore, the US Army issued a light observation helicopter (LOH) requirement for a machine to replace not only its current force of Bell H-13 and Hiller H-23 light helicopters, but also its fleet of Cessna L-17 Bird Dog liaison and forward air control (FAC) aircraft. The requirement specified a turbine engine, cruising speed of 127mph (204km/h), endurance of 3 hours in the observation role, ability to hover at 6,000ft (1,830m) out of ground effect, and an exacting combination of low cost and easy maintenance.

The size of the order in prospect was very large, and the requirement elicited 22 design proposals from no fewer than 12 American helicopter manufacturers. In 1961 the US Army ordered five prototypes from each of three companies. The designs of the Bell YHO-4A (from 1962 YOH-4A) and Hiller YHO-5A (from 1962 YOH-5A) were clearly influenced by the two companies' considerable experience with piston-engined helicopters, but the Hughes YHO-6A (from 1962 YOH-6A) was of altogether more advanced concept; the company's sole successful helicopter to date, the Model 269, was just entering production.

The team that designed the Model 369, as the YOH-6A was known to Hughes at this time, had decided to concentrate on an advanced yet simple main rotor, high manoeuvrability and low drag. The main rotor was of an unusual part-hingeless four-blade configuration with conventional flapping and feathering hinges replaced by 15 flexible stainless steel straps connecting the two pairs of diametrically opposed blades set at 90 degrees to each other. This rotor core required no maintenance, lacked the complexity of conventional rotor cores, and offered advantages such as better control response, lower vibration and smaller diameter. The use of a four-blade rotor also allowed a more optimised blade design and thus better controllability, which in turn meant that the Model 369 could use a manual control system without hydraulic boost or any need for a stability-augmentation system. The use of a small main rotor also meant that the size of the tail rotor could be reduced and carried on a shorter and lighter tail boom. Low drag was provided by the teardrop shape of the main fuselage, which was sized to the width of two men, and fully enclosed the engine that was located at an angle of 45 degrees in the rear of the pod, with the drive shaft terminating in a bevel gear on the common shaft driving the main and tail rotors.

The structural core of the design was the payload compartment, a light alloy unit under the main rotor and accommodating folding seats for two passengers: the roof of this unit supported the fixed rotor mast, its front bulkhead supported the pilots' seats, its rear bulkhead supported the engine, the lower corners of the two bulkheads carried the legs for the twin-skid landing gear, and the floor carried the fuel tanks and batteries. Considerable care went into the streamlining of the fuselage pod, and even the short main rotor mast was nicely faired into the forward part of the boom that projected from the upper rear of the main pod to carry the tail unit, which comprised a small rotor on the port side of the boom, a vertical tail surface with large and small sections above and below the boom respectively, and a starboard-side stabilizer braced to the upper fin at an outward angle of 45 degrees.

First flown in February 1963, the YOH-6A was several hundreds of pounds lighter than either of its competitors but had the same maximum take-off weight, translating into greater payload with the same engine. The YOH-6A was also smaller, faster, longer-ranged, more manoeuvrable and easier to fly than the YOH-4A and YOH-5A, and after a seven-month competitive evaluation was declared winner of the LOH competition in May 1965, when the US Army placed an initial order for 714 OH-6A Cayuse helicopters out of an expected total of more than 4,000.

In the following month, Hughes announced a civil version as the Model 500 with the Allison 250-C18 version of the military helicopter's T63-A-5 turboshaft. These two engines were mechanically identical, but the civil model had a higher sea-level rating as the military model was derated by 20 per cent for constant power at higher altitudes and higher temperatures.

The OH-6A entered service in September 1966, and in the Vietnam War soon proved itself a superb operator in its designed role. All was not well with the production programme, however, as increased demand for fixed- and rotary-winged aircraft at this time was badly affecting the aerospace industry in the south-western part of the USA, where skilled manpower was soon in short supply, as were materials and many bought-in components. The result was a steep rise in production cost and a sharp decline in production tempo, and in 1967 the US Army was sufficiently unhappy with the situation to reopen the LOH competition.

This time, Bell won with the Model 206A JetRanger that it had evolved as an improved version of the YOH-4A (Model 206) for the civil market. The Bell helicopter was ordered into production as the OH-58A Kiowa, and

The McDonnell Douglas (originally Hughes) Model 500MD Defender is an export type offering capabilities similar to those of the OH-6D Kiowa Warrior with its mast-mounted sight and external provision for weapons including four BGM-71 TOW heavyweight wire-guided anti-tank missiles.

The light helicopters of the McDonnell Douglas Model 500 series originated as the Hughes Model 369 that was accepted for US Army service as the OH-6 Cayuse in the observation role, and are now notable for their excellent combination of performance, quietness and operating economy. This is a Model 500MD Defender for the export market with a mast-mounted sight allowing target surveillance, acquisition and designation as the helicopter hovers behind cover.

production of the OH-6A ended in August 1970 after the delivery of 1,434 helicopters. Even so, the type became the most popular helicopter of the Vietnam War, but was phased out of first-line service after the war so that regular army units could standardise on the OH-58A. Most of the OH-6As were passed to National Guard units, and many survive into the 1990s, a considerable number having been converted to alternative roles with the baseline designations AH-6 (armed support of Special Forces' operations), EH-6 (electronic reconnaissance), and MH-6 (infiltration/exfiltration of Special Forces as well as armed support).

The Model 500 was introduced in 1968 as the civil counterpart of the OH-6A, with a powerplant of one 317hp (236kW) Allison 250-C18A turboshaft derated to 278hp (207kW) for take-off and 243hp (181kW) for continuous running and, in the export version, for limited military applications such as casevac. The type has been developed in both American- and licence-built forms through a number of steadily more capable versions with uprated powerplants, and has also spawned dedicated military variants for the export market.

The first of these was the Model 500M that was the dedicated military export variant of the Model 500C, powered by the Allison 250-C18A turboshaft derated to 275hp (207kW). The type was built under licence in Argentina as the RACA (Hughes) 500M, in Italy as the BredaNardi NH-500M and also as the NH-500MC with hot-and-high features, and in Japan as the Kawasaki (Hughes) 500M (service designation OH-6J).

The Model 500MD Defender is an uprated military variant based on the Model 500D with the 420hp (313kW) Allison 250-C20B turboshaft, a five-blade main rotor, a T-tail and other improvements. The type was aimed at the market niche for light multi-role helicopters and first flew in 1976, and its success is attested not only by deliveries from the parent factory but also by licensed production in Italy as the BredaNardi (Hughes) NH-500MD and in South Korea as the Korean Air (Hughes) 500MD. The Defender can be used in a number of forms for virtually the whole gamut of battlefield and naval tasks, and was offered with options such as armoured seats, the Hughes 'Black Hole Ocarina' IR suppressor for the exhaust, self-sealing fuel tanks, a structural beam attached to the after side of the rear bulkhead and projecting upward and outward from each side of the fuselage for the carriage of disposable stores on two hardpoints, and port-side provision for armament ranging in calibre from the 0.3in (7.62mm) M134 Minigun in the McDonnell Douglas Helicopters (Hughes) HGS-5 package based on the OH-6A's M27 package, via the 30mm McDonnell Douglas Helicopters (Hughes) M230 Chain Gun, to the 40mm McDonnell Douglas (Hughes) M129 grenade-launcher in the McDonnell Douglas Helicopters (Hughes) M8 package; the HGS-5 package can be replaced by the HGS-55 package containing one 0.3in McDonnell Douglas Helicopters (Hughes) EX-34 Chain Gun with 2,000 rounds in a fuselage magazine.

The type was also developed in a number of specialised subvariants such as the Model 500MD Scout Defender for battlefield reconnaissance and light attack with 'Black Hole Ocarina' IR suppression, a nose-mounted stabilized sight, and provision for a wide assortment of light armament items including multiple launchers for unguided rockets and a gun up to 30mm calibre; the Model 500MD Quiet Advanced Scout Defender, similar to the Scout Defender but with noise reduction features and a mast-mounted sight for nap-of-the-earth flight profiles; the Model 500MD/TOW Defender dedicated anti-tank version with four BGM-71 TOW missiles and appropriate sight; the Model 500MD/MMS-TOW Defender, similar to the Model 500MD/TOW but with a mast-mounted sight on a pylon 2ft (0.61m) above the rotor head; the Model 500MD/ASW Defender dedicated ASW variant with search radar, MAD and two Mk 46 torpedoes; and the Model 500MD Defender II upgraded model with FIM-92 Stinger lightweight AAMs for self-defence, and fitted for items such as a mast-mounted sight, FLIR and an RWR.

The Model 500MG Defender is an improved multi-role military export version with a revised and sharper nose profile, advanced avionics, and the 420hp (313kW) Allison 250-C20B turboshaft driving a rotor system based on that of the Model 500E.

The Model 520N is the no tail rotor (NOTAR) version of the Model 500 – torque control is effected by the engine exhaust, which is ducted to the tail and ejected through the port side of the boom via Coanda slots and steering louvres. Overall, the system reduces complexity, vulnerability and power loss. A military variant of the Model 520N was developed in South Korea as the Korean Air (McDonnell Douglas) Model 520MK Black Tiger, but no details have been released.

The Model 530MG Defender is the military version of the Model 530F, with an advanced cockpit incorporating the Racal RAMS 3000 integrated display and control system (based on a digital databus to allow the use of the latest weapons), mast-mounted sight and a removable beam with provision for a wide assortment of weapons.

Top and above: One of the most important operational tasks that can be undertaken by the McDonnell Douglas Model 500MD Defender series is the battlefield anti-tank role. This is achieved in the Model 500MD/TOW Defender subvariant with a quartet of BGM-71 TOW heavyweight anti-tank missiles carried in external pairs and guided via wires using targeting information provided by means of the nose-mounted stabilized sight.

The type that replaced the OH-6A in production from 1968 was the Bell OH-58A Kiowa, derived ultimately from the D-250 design originally offered for the US Army's 1960 LOH requirement. The D-250 became the Model 206 in hardware and was evaluated as the YHO-4A, later YOH-4A, which was a trim all-metal type of orthodox pod-and-boom construction with twin-skid landing gear and a dynamic system of typical Bell design, including a two-blade main rotor (with stabilizing bar at right angles to the blades) powered by one 250hp (186kW) Allison T63-A-5 turboshaft. The first YOH-4A flew in December 1962, but the type was rejected in favour of the Hughes Model 369 (HO-6, later OH-6). This was a setback for Bell, but the company had already decided to prepare a civil version with a redesigned fuselage as the Model 206A. This had a more streamlined fuselage that replaced the Model 206's completely glazed and virtually hemispherical nose with a more conventional forward fuselage carrying a stepped windscreen, and faired the boom into the pod part in a less utilitarian manner. The Model 206A was launched with a powerplant of one 317hp (236kW) Allison 250-C18A turboshaft driving a revised semi-rigid rotor of increased diameter and not carrying a stabilizing bar. Construction of a prototype began in July 1965, and this machine first took to the air in December of the same year. Certification followed in October 1966, and deliveries began in January 1967. By this time, production of the OH-6A had run into cost and delivery difficulties, so the US Army reopened the LOH competition, in which Bell entered the Model 206A that was declared winner in March 1968. The US Army then placed orders for some 2,200 helicopters with the service designation OH-58A Kiowa. The type entered service from May 1969 with a powerplant of one 317hp (236kW) Allison T63-A-700 turboshaft and accommodation for two persons plus freight in the rear of the cabin.

Production lasted to 1974, and as a result of an improvement programme launched by the US Army in 1976, the OH-58C appeared as the OH-58A converted with flat-plate canopy for reduced glint, an uprated powerplant for better hot-and-high performance, and a 'black hole' IR reduction package to improve survivability against IR-homing missiles. Successful evaluation of three OH-58As modified to this standard resulted in the decision to convert another 435 helicopters, and this programme was completed by March 1985.

At the end of the 1970s the US Army became increasingly concerned about the continued viability of its scouting helicopter capability, and launched the Army helicopter improvement Program (AHIP) to provide a near-term scout helicopter (NTSH) that would bridge the operational gap until the advent of the planned light helicopter experimental (LHX) that was later ordered as the Boeing/Sikorsky RAH-66 Comanche. There were several suggestions for the required type, but in September 1981 the US Army announced that the Bell Model 406 Aeroscout proposal had been accepted and that five prototypes would be evaluated.

This proposal was based on a radical upgrade of the OH-58C Kiowa military version of the Model 206 light helicopter, with an updated avionics package and a considerably more powerful engine driving an advanced four-blade main rotor with composite-structure blades. The avionics package was based on two systems, namely the Honeywell Sperry cockpit control and display system, and the McDonnell Douglas/Northrop mast-mounted sight (MMS) system. The former is used in association with improved communication and navigation systems (including Doppler navigation and a strapdown INS), digital moving-map display, target hand-off system, and night vision goggles. The latter combines a magnifying TV camera, imaging FLIR sensor, boresight system, and a combined laser ranger and designator system for use in finding and designating targets to be engaged with laser-homing missiles fired by friendly air or ground forces.

The complete OH-58D package thus provides commanders with a real-time combat information, command and control, reconnaissance, aerial observation, and target acquisition/designation capability for operation with attack helicopters, air cavalry and field artillery units by day and night even under adverse weather conditions. A key feature in this important overall capability is the location of the sensor unit above the main rotor, as this increases the helicopter's survivability by allowing the machine to hover behind trees or masking terrain with only its MMS protruding.

The first of five prototype conversions flew in October 1983, and 376 (originally to have been 578, then reduced to 477 and finally to the figure quoted above) helicopters are being produced as OH-58A conversions and new-build machines to this AHIP standard, which includes the military version of the Allison 250-C30R turboshaft.

The MMS allows the OH-58D to scout for the McDonnell Douglas AH-64

The mast-mounted sight that can be fitted on the light helicopters of the McDonnell Douglas Model 500MD Defender series has a minimum effect on flight performance and agility, but provides the opportunity for considerably improved survivability by allowing the crew to operate effectively in the tactical sense without revealing the bulk of their helicopter for detection and engagement by the enemy's anti-aircraft defences.

Apache, the typical teaming being three OH-58Ds leading five AH-64As, for whose AGM-114 Hellfire ASMs the OH-58Ds acquire and designate targets.

In December 1987 the US Army began to operate 15 examples of an upgraded version of the OH-58D in interim armed form as the OH-58D Kiowa Prime Chance or Armed OH-58D Kiowa. Created from September 1987, this configuration with clearance for the standard four types of Kiowa Warrior armament was designed to provide the US forces operating in the Persian Gulf with a capability against Iranian high-speed gunboats harassing shipping in this area in the closing stages of the Iraqi-Iranian Gulf War (1980-88).

The full production standard, as delivered from the 208th OH-58D, is now designated OH-58D Kiowa Warrior with the Allison 250-C30X turboshaft, ALQ-144(V)1 IR jammer and two lateral hardpoints able to carry four weapon types. These last are four AGM-114A Hellfire ASMs/anti-tank missiles, or four FIM-92A Stinger short-range AAMs, or two multiple launchers each carrying seven 2.75in (70mm) Hydra 70 unguided rockets, or two Global Helicopter Technology CFD-5000 pods each carrying one 0.5in (12.7mm) Colt-Browning M3 heavy machine gun or two 0.3in (7.62mm) machine guns, or a combination of these weapon types. The Stinger is used in conjunction with the Thomson-CSF/Hamilton Standard VH-100 ATAS (Air-To-Air Stinger) wide-angle HUD.

It is planned that all OH-58D Kiowas will eventually be upgraded to OH-58D Kiowa Warrior armed standard, 81 of them in an OH-58D Kiowa Warrior multi-purpose light helicopter (MPLH) configuration for special missions including casevac (with four externally carried litters), troop transport (with six externally carried outward-facing seats) and other roles in low-intensity warfare. Other features of the MPLH version are folding main rotor blades, a folding tailplane and a tilting fin to facilitate loading into tactical transport aircraft.

The two major trends in modern helicopter design both derive ultimately from American experience with rotorcraft in Vietnam. Firstly helicopters have become combat aircraft and therefore need heavy gun and missile armament. The only armed helicopters before this time were anti-submarine types operating from shore bases and warships, for which torpedo and depth charge weapons proved easy to install; and second, the use of helicopters in the combat zone made it clear that manoeuvrability and speed had to be improved.

To meet the need for heavier and better armament, helicopters sprouted a variety of stub wings and other protuberances to hold weapons. These additions had an adverse effect on performance, and stub wings are now designed more carefully to minimise drag and thus impede performance as little as possible. The increased use of advanced avionics has led to a revision of the basic fuselage shape, which, in modern combat helicopters such as the HueyCobra and later developments, resembles a conventional combat aeroplane more than typical examples of the older helicopter types.

Designed as the AAFSS, the Lockheed AH-56 Cheyenne mentioned above was a notable example of this trend. Speed was enhanced to a maximum of 244mph (393km/h) through the adoption of a retractable landing gear arrangement, a potent powerplant in the form of one 3,925hp (2,926kW) General Electric T64 turboshaft, and a novel lift/thrust concept: as the helicopter translated into forward flight, an increasing proportion of the lift burden was entrusted to the large stub wing, allowing power to be diverted from the main rotor to the large pusher propeller located at the extreme tail. Apart from a heavy load of avionics, the Cheyenne also carried a formidable array of guns, bombs, guided missiles and grenade-launchers. The model never entered production or service, being too costly and

complex, but it formed the conceptual basis from which was evolved the requirement for the advanced attack helicopter (AAH).

This requirement led to the Hughes Model 77 that first flew in 1975 and entered service as the AH-64 Apache, now a product of the McDonnell Douglas company since its purchase of the Hughes helicopter division. The Apache is a smaller, lighter and less powerful machine than the Cheyenne, but at the same time is fully effective as a result of its advanced design, thoroughly modern avionics and potent weapons. The type's main operator is the US Army, with which the Apache serves as a battlefield type specialising in the destruction of tanks with the Rockwell AGM-114 Hellfire missile, which has semi-active laser guidance and considerable stand-off range. First flown in September 1975, the Apache is thus the US Army's most important battlefield helicopter.

The concept of the armed helicopter was far from new when the Model 77 was schemed, for armament schemes had been planned for the first operational helicopters in World War II; the French had made extensive used of armed helicopters in the North African campaigns that ended in the early 1960s; and in 1965 the Bell AH-1 HueyCobra was about to enter service as the US Army's first rotary-wing warplane. What worried the planners of the US Army, however, was the fact that the HueyCobra resembled its predecessors in lacking all-weather flight and weapon-delivery capabilities, and in defensive terms was limited to light armour sufficient to provide protection only against small-arms fire.

The most important task faced by the US Army at that time, however, was spearheading the NATO defence of Western Europe against the threat of communist aggression by the Soviet-dominated forces of the Warsaw Pact. Such aggression would certainly exploit any tactical advantage offered at night or in poor weather conditions, and would use the very latest in heavily armoured battlefield vehicles. As adverse-weather operation and the defeat of heavy armour both lay beyond the HueyCobra's capabilities, it was clear that a more capable battlefield helicopter was needed. This had to possess the ability to fly and acquire targets under all weather and light conditions, to carry weapons

Above and right: With its size and aggressive appearance, the McDonnell Douglas AH-64A Apache offers little in the way of aesthetic appeal but is nonetheless a highly capable battlefield helicopter as proved in the 1991 UN-led campaign to expel the Iraqi aggressors from Kuwait. In this campaign the AH-64A revealed good reliability and devastating offensive capability, the latter resulting from the use of the underfuselage 30mm Hughes 'Chain Gun' cannon for the destruction of soft-skinned and lightly armoured vehicles as well as the elimination of air-defence elements, and of the Rockwell AGM-114A Hellfire semi-active laser-homing missile for the elimination of battle tanks.

capable of defeating the heaviest armour, and had to be fitted with the means of avoiding or surviving the attentions of modern battlefield anti-aircraft weapons.

The 1969 cancellation of the Cheyenne gave the US Army planners a chance to re-examine the requirement to which the AH-56 had been designed, and which was considered as having been too ambitious for the current state-of-the-art technologies. The planners' object was now to draw up a requirement for a more practical battlefield helicopter that would also be cheaper to buy and operate. Two early casualties of this simplification process were the need to escort other helicopters and provide them with protection against air as well as surface threats, and the need for very high speed. Elements of the requirement that were not relaxed, however, were agility (including rate of climb) and long endurance in fully armed configuration. The former was seen as the single most important factor in evading detection and consequent destruction through employment of nap-of-the-earth flight techniques and manoeuvres too tight to be followed by the tracking systems of missiles and anti-aircraft artillery.

In 1972 the US Army issued its resulting AAH requirement. Of the several companies that responded to the associated request for proposals, Bell and Hughes were each contracted to build two flying and one static-test prototypes as the YAH-63A and YAH-64A respectively, each powered by two examples of the turboshaft specially developed for this application as the General Electric GE.12 but later placed in production as the T700. Bell's Model 309 KingCobra clearly drew on the company's experience with the Model 209 (AH-1 HueyCobra), but adopted tricycle landing gear and reversed the positions of

105

The losing contender in the US Army's Advanced Attack Helicopter competition won by the Hughes YAH-64A was the Bell YAH-63A, designed as the Model 309 KingCobra with tricycle landing gear and the crew arranged with the gunner behind and above the pilot.

the crew so that the pilot was seated in the front seat ahead of and below the co-pilot/gunner. Hughes also drew on its own experience, in this instance with the diminutive Model 369 (OH-6 Cayuse), but added features from its own assessment of the AH-1 HueyCobra (including tandem seating with the pilot in the rear seat above and behind the co-pilot/gunner) and opted for fixed tailwheel landing gear. Hughes also teamed with Teledyne Ryan and Menasco: the former was responsible for the design and manufacture of the fuselage, tail unit and weapon-carrying stub wings, while the latter was entrusted with responsibility for the landing gear that was designed to absorb the stresses of a crash landing or a heavy landing on sloped surfaces, and was also intended to fold upward to reduce overall height when the helicopter was partially disassembled for transport in a cargo aeroplane.

As prime contractor and therefore responsible for the overall design, Hughes planned its Model 77 with a structure that was as conventional as possible in an effort to simplify construction and keep cost under tight rein. Thus most of the airframe was planned in light alloy semi-monocoque construction with redundant load-carrying paths to reduce the effect of damage from hits by projectiles in calibres up to 23mm. The crew seats were designed in Kevlar armour, and additional protection was afforded by boron armour under and around the cockpit section, and by an acrylic blast barrier between the two sections.

The advanced dynamic system drew heavily on the company's experience with the Model 369, and was based on a five-blade main rotor and a four-blade tail rotor, the latter with the blades set not at 90 degrees to each other but at 55 and 125 degrees for reduced noise.

The first of the two flight-test YAH-64A prototypes flew in September 1975 with a powerplant of two 1,536hp (1,145kW) T700-GE-701 turboshafts. It had been planned that competitive evaluation of the YAH-63A and YAH-64A would lead to a production decision in 1979, but in December 1976 the YAH-64A was declared winner and three more prototypes were ordered with a revised tail unit on which the fixed-incidence tailplane was moved to the top of the vertical tail surface in a T-tail arrangement. The vertical surface underwent considerable modification during the flight test programme, and the stabilizer eventually reverted to a low-set position, although it was now located behind the vertical surface and became an all-moving unit.

The real operational capabilities of the AH-64, which was named Apache in 1981, depend on its avionics, and Hughes decided that most of the electronic bays should be located externally in box fairings along the low sides of the forward fuselage. These fairings had to be enlarged several times, and eventually reached back under the stub wing, whose trailing edges were fitted with high-deflection flaps that were later deleted.

Another part of the design that underwent steady change was the nose, which accommodated the two most important groups of sensors, those for the target acquisition and designation system (TADS) and PNVS. Northrop and Martin Marietta competed for these complex systems, Martin Marietta winning in April 1982. The two independent systems are both turret-mounted in the extreme nose and feed data to the two members of the crew via the monocle screen carried by the helmet of the IHADSS.

The TADS is based on a nose turret that can be traversed 120 degrees left and right of the centreline and elevated in an arc between -60 and +30 degrees. The turret accommodates daylight and night/all-weather sensors in its port and starboard halves respectively. The daylight sensors comprise a TV camera with wide- and narrow-angle fields of vision, direct-view optics with wide- and narrow-angle fields of vision, a laser spot tracker, and an International Laser Systems laser ranger and designator, while the night/adverse-weather sensor is an FLIR with wide-, medium- and narrow-angle fields of vision. In short, the TADS provides for the optronic, optical or thermal acquisition of targets that can then be laser-ranged and laser-designated to allow manual or automatic tracking for autonomous engagement with the cannon, missiles or rockets.

It is worth noting, moreover, that while the TADS is designed primarily for the co-pilot/gunner, it provides back-up night vision capability for the pilot in the event of a failure in the PNVS. The latter is based on an FLIR in a separate turret located above the TADS turret, and this sensor's 20- and 40-degree field of vision provides high-resolution thermal imaging for day/night nap-of-the-earth flight profiles under all weather conditions.

The co-pilot/gunner is primarily responsible for the armament, which comprises disposable stores carried on the four underwing hardpoints and the 30mm cannon in an underfuselage installation designed to collapse upward between the two crew members in the event of a crash landing. The pilot can override the co-pilot/gunner in use of the weapons, but his principal task is flying the helicopter with the aid of the highly advanced all-weather systems. This is only one part of the Apache's comprehensive electronics, which also include an RWR, active jammers, chaff/flare dispensers, an IR jammer, and a laser warning system.

The development phase of the AH-64 programme was successfully completed in August 1981, and the first AH-64A production helicopters were delivered in February 1984 with a powerplant of two 1,696hp (1,265kW) T700-GE-701 turboshafts. Operational service has confirmed that while it is large, complex and costly, the AH-64A is a highly capable machine offering advanced sensors and useful performance for the very accurate delivery of a heavy ordnance load. The disposable load is optimised for the destruction of hard- and soft-skinned vehicles on the battlefield, while the underfuselage cannon is designed for the suppression of enemy ground defences. Particular advantages of the design are high survivability, good protection of the crew and primary systems, and sophisticated avionics such as the TADS and PNVS.

The manufacturer, which is now the McDonnell Douglas Helicopter Company after the McDonnell Douglas Corporation's January 1984 purchase of Hughes Helicopters Inc., has proposed that the type be retrofitted under a three-stage programme with the GPS, improved Doppler navigation, and enhanced versions of the TADS and PNVS. From the hundredth helicopter, the basic standard has been improved by the use of composite-construction main rotor blades, and since the late 1980s all

Tackling the Battlefield Helicopter

SUCH is the threat of the helicopter, within the context of operations on the modern high-intensity battlefield, that there has developed a see-saw technological competition between the helicopter and battlefield air-defence weapons. The object of the battlefield helicopter is to reach the battlefield, observe, acquire and/or designate the required target(s) and then, in the case of an attack helicopter, destroy the target(s) before exiting the scene. On the other side of the ground/air interface, the task of battlefield air-defence systems is to find, acquire, engage and destroy such helicopters before they can undertake their primary task. Helicopters and helicopter-launched weapons were developed with higher performance and with a sturdier structure better able to absorb combat damage, a measure of armour protection, crashworthy features such as impact-tolerant seats and fuel systems, countermeasures designed to reduce the efficiency of ground-fired weapons, mast-mounted sights so that the helicopter could both fly and operate in nap-of-the-earth mode, and improved weapons offering higher velocity and longer stand-off range as well as improved operational features such as a fire-and-forget capability or the ability to home on a target designated by a third party. All these factors helped to reduce the time the helicopter had to spend in the danger zone, extend the range from which the helicopter could tackle its target, and curtail the efficiency of the smaller number of weapons that could still be employed against the helicopter. The designers of anti-helicopter weapons then responded with improved, longer-range equipments such as fast-firing 40mm anti-aircraft guns firing specially designed ammunition with the aid of a more advanced fire-control system, and surface-to-air missiles with counter-countermeasures and/or un-jammable laser guidance. The balance between the helicopter and ground defences is now finely balanced with the tilt perhaps slightly in favour of the battlefield helicopter because of its low observability and ability to deliver fire-and-forget weapons at significant stand-off range.

Apaches have had upgraded self-protection capability in the form of four FIM-92A Stinger lightweight AAMs attached (two on each side) to the outboard underwing pylons.

The AH-64B Apache designation was first postulated for an improved version to be delivered in the mid-to-late 1990s with voice-actuated controls, a fly-by-light fibre-optical control system using a four-axis side-arm control stick, improved armament including a pair of AIM-9 Sidewinder AAMs, a GPS receiver, Doppler radar, improved night vision equipment, an advanced composite rotor hub, and a reinforced thermoplastic secondary structure.

The designation was then applied to 254 AH-64As, upgraded to reflect the lessons learned in the 1991 UN-led war with Iraq, and thus revised with GPS, improved radios, target hand-off capability, improved navigation, and greater reliability including new rotor blades. In the event, however, the revised designation was not applied to these upgraded machines.

The AH-64C Apache designation was reserved for an initial 308 AH-64As retrofitted to virtual AH-64D standard except for the omission of the Longbow radar (for which provision is nonetheless made) and the retention of the T700-GE-701 turboshafts. Late in 1993 the designation was abandoned, and all 562 upgraded AH-64A helicopters are now known by the designation AH-64D.

The AH-64D Longbow Apache is an improved version of the AH-64A/B with a powerplant of two 1,800hp (1,342kW) T700-GE-701C turboshafts and the Longbow fire-control system based on a Westinghouse millimetric-wavelength radar with its antenna in a mast-mounted radome above the main rotor. This radar is the primary sensor of the Longbow system (initially designated Airborne Adverse-Weather Weapon System), and is intended for rapid target-area search, automatic detection and classification of targets, and all-weather fire-and-forget engagement with a revised version of the Hellfire missile, namely the radar-homing Longbow Hellfire that carries – in addition to its semi-active laser seeker modified for improved resistance to optical countermeasures – a combined radio-frequency and IR seeker as well as a warhead optimised for the penetration of modern types of advanced tank protection.

The AH-64D will also carry lightweight AAMs (originally to have been FIM-92A Stinger weapons but now possibly to be Shorts Starstreak weapons) on the tips of its stub wings, and will have avionics based on a digital databus. It is also possible that the AH-64D will introduce features from the cancelled Apache Plus programme such as a redesigned cockpit, a larger forward avionics bay for improved electronics, and a digital fly-by-wire system developed by General Electric and Lucas.

Although it was the Americans who took an early lead in the development of manoeuvrable and heavily armed combat helicopters, the USSR began to whittle away this technical lead with the Mi-24 'Hind-D' gunship version of the Mi-24 'Hind' assault transport helicopter. Although large and relatively unmanoeuvrable by comparison with the American helicopters, the 'Hind-D' has the same type of narrow fuselage with a stepped cockpit arrangement, and among its virtues are good weapon-aiming systems and the ability to carry a heavy load of multiple weapon types.

In origin the Mi-24 is a multi-role helicopter, and has been the subject of contested evaluations in the West, in relation largely to the tactical capability of the gunship models. The type is based on the dynamic system of the Mi-14 and Mi-17, using two TV2-117 (later TV3-117) turboshafts, in this application married to a new fuselage of slender lines to enhance performance and battlefield survivability. The Mi-24A initial model, also known by the NATO reporting designation 'Hind-A', has a crew of three

The McDonnell Douglas AH-64A Apache is no longer in the first flush of its operational youth, but is still an extremely capable battlefield helicopter offering its operator high performance, high-quality flight and combat electronics and optronics, and a carefully balanced blend of short- and medium-range offensive weapons.

(pilot, co-pilot/gunner and ground engineer), and can carry an eight-man infantry squad in its hold. The 'Hind-A' was in fact the second production model, the initial Mi-24B 'Hind-B' having been a pre-production type built only in small numbers for service from 1973, and distinguishable from the 'Hind-A' by its straight wings with only four hardpoints, and by the location of the tail rotor on the starboard side of the fin.

The 'Hind-A' has an anhedraled wing with four underwing hardpoints and two overwing twin launchers for AT-3 'Swatter' anti-tank missiles, and a 0.5in (12.7mm) DShK heavy machine gun (slaved to the undernose sight system) is installed in the nose. It is unlikely that the survivors of the 'Hind-A' and 'Hind-B' variants are still used for the infantry assault role, a more likely task being the battlefield movement of anti-tank missile teams, and the Mi-24U 'Hind-C' is the dual-control trainer version of the 'Hind-A' without the nose gun and wing-tip missile launcher rails. Production of the Mi-24A and Mi-24U totalled about 250 helicopters between 1973 and 1977.

First seen by Western observers in 1977, the Mi-24 'Hind-D' helicopter is the much-altered version used in the dedicated gunship role, with a new upper forward fuselage featuring stepped cockpits for the gunner (nose) and pilot (behind and slightly above the gunner). The gunner controls a 0.5in (12.7mm) rotary four-barrel heavy machine gun in an undernose turret slaved to the adjacent KPS-53A optronic sighting pod for air-to-surface and air-to-air use, while the wing-mounted armament is similar to that of the 'Hind-A', although more extensive. The sensor fit for the accurate firing of air-to-surface ordnance includes an air data probe, low-light-level TV, radar and a laser tracker. Although the cabin can carry an eight-man infantry squad, it is likely that only one man and reload weapons are carried for battlefield replenishment of the underwing hardpoints.

The type clearly possesses considerable speed and offensive capability, but Western analysts point out that the 'Hind-D' is large and relatively lacking in manoeuvrability for the gunship role. Soviet experience with the type in Afghanistan led to the adoption under the tail boom of a dispenser loaded with 192 IR decoys for heat-seeking missiles, as well as an IR jammer and RWR. A training version of the Mi-24D is the Mi-24DU, which differs externally from the baseline gunship in its lack of the undernose machine gun turret. Production totalled about 350 helicopters between 1973 and 1977.

The Mi-24V 'Hind-E' is an improved Mi-24D version produced in two subvariants for service from 1976, with more specialised avionics and optronics including the ASP-17V automatic missile guidance pod under the nose with a searchlight in its rear section, and the pilot's reflector sight replaced by an HUD. The type also possesses upgraded systems, improved defensive features, and a modified combination of underwing and overwing hardpoints for up to eight AT-6 'Spiral' instead of AT-2 'Swatter' anti-tank missiles under the wings and AA-8 'Aphid' short-range AAMs on the overwing rails.

The Mi-24VP 'Hind-E' is a subvariant with the rotary four-barrel heavy machine gun replaced by a 23mm GSh-23L cannon with 450 rounds of ammunition. About 1,000 Mi-24V and Mi-24VP helicopters were built between 1976 and 1986.

The Mi-24P 'Hind-F' is a Mi-24V version that entered service in 1981 with a revised nose in which the undernose machine gun turret is removed, its space nicely faired so that primary emphasis is placed on the heavier capability provided by one two-barrel cannon (originally thought to be a 23mm GSh-23L but now known to be a 30mm GSh-30-2) with 750 rounds in a pack fixed on the starboard side of the nose. As a result of Soviet experience in Afghanistan during the 1980s, the type is also fitted with a number of measures to defeat heat-seeking SAMs; these measures include inlet and exhaust shrouds, a dorsally mounted 'hot brick' IR jammer and stub wing-mounted dispensers for IR decoy flares. Deliveries amounted to about 620 helicopters between 1981 and 1990.

The Mi-24RSh 'Hind-G1' is the specialised radiation-sampling variant, and about 150 such helicopters were built between 1983 and 1989. The Mi-24K 'Hind-G2' is a variant of the Mi-24RSh with a large starboard-facing camera in the cabin, and is believed to be used for the tactical reconnaissance and artillery-spotting roles. About 150 such helicopters were completed between 1983 and 1989. The Mi-24BMT 'Hind-?' was introduced in 1973 as a conversion of older helicopters for the minesweeping role. Other 'Hind' variants include the Mi-25 'Hind-D' export version of the Mi-24D with avionics of a reduced standard; the Mi-35 'Hind-E' export version of the Mi-24V with additional armour for the crew and vital dynamic system components, a heavier weapon load carried on six hardpoints, different avionics, and inbuilt chaff/flare launchers rather than the boom-mounted IR jammer of Soviet models; the Mi-35P 'Hind-F' export version of the Mi-24P; and the Mi-35M 'Hind-?' latest air mobility version for the Russian army, with the dynamic system of the Mil Mi-28 'Havoc' attack helicopter, a revised undernose turret carrying a 23mm GSh-23L two-barrel cannon, and a revised suite of avionics.

By the early 1980s the Soviets had evaluated the concept of combat helicopters and began to develop specialised types that were developed slowly throughout the decade for a possible service debut in the mid-to-late 1990s as the Kamov Ka-50 and Mil Mi-28.

The Ka-50, offered for sale with the name Werewolf and also known by the NATO reporting name 'Hokum-A', was designed with the co-axial twin rotors typical of Kamov practice and was initially known by the supposed designation Ka-41. The Ka-50 first flew in July 1982 in the form of the V-80 prototype for an advanced battlefield helicopter of which relatively few details are available. In combination with a slim fuselage and retractable landing gear, the rotor design offers a high degree of agility and speed, while the elimination of the tail rotor offers the advantages of a shorter fuselage for reduced battlefield visibility and vulnerability.

Although it was originally thought that the type was tasked with the anti-helicopter escort role over the land battlefield, in conjunction with offensive operations by Mi-24 'Hind' and Mi-28 'Havoc' helicopters, the Ka-50 was later assessed as a shipborne type designed to provide Naval Infantry amphibious assault forces with close air support over the beach-head. In 1992, however, the Russians finally revealed that the type had indeed been developed in competition with the Mi-28 and had been selected in preference to that type as successor to the Mi-24 'Hind-D'.

The Ka-50's cockpit, powerplant and transmission are protected by two layers of structural armour weighing some 772lb (330kg) and capable of withstanding the effects of 20mm cannon shells, and a notable feature is the installation of an ejector seat as the main component of an escape system that ensures explosive separation of the two rigid rotors' six blades at the moment of seat initiation. The Ka-50 is unique as the world's first single-seat attack/anti-tank helicopter to enter full production, and its electronics (including provision for third-party target acquisition) are optimised for the easing of the pilot's workload.

The cannon barbette on the port side of the nose can be elevated and depressed by a hydraulic system but has no traverse capability, so the complete helicopter is yawed to aim the weapon and then held on target by a tracking system that turns the helicopter on its vertical axis. The cannon

Accorded the Western reporting name 'Havoc', the Mil Mi-28 two-seat battlefield helicopter has been ordered by the air arm of the Commonwealth of Independent States after a complicated tussle with the Kamov Ka-50 'Hokum' single-seat combat helicopter that was also ordered, albeit at a slightly earlier date, and had also been offered on the export market with the name Werewolf. The Mi-28 is typical of modern battlefield helicopters in placing general operational utility above outright flight performance, and for this reason the helicopter is somewhat ungainly in appearance although clearly still a very formidable machine that has also been developed into a Mi-28N version with a mast-mounted sight and other enhancement for full operational capability at night and under adverse weather conditions.

is the same weapon as already used in the BMP infantry fighting vehicle, and is thus heavier than an equivalent weapon designed solely for aerial use, but is notably rugged under dusty and hot conditions and is a dual-feed weapon able to fire HE incendiary and armour-piercing ammunition.

The whole machine was designed for deployment away from base for at least two weeks without need of maintenance ground equipment, as all refuelling and servicing of the avionics and weapons can be undertaken from ground level.

The 'Hokum-B' is the two-seat conversion trainer derivative of the 'Hokum-A', retaining full combat capability and therefore accommodating a pilot and trainee or weapon operator side-by-side in a widened forward fuselage section.

First flown in November 1982 for service from the mid-1990s, the Mi-28 'Havoc' seems to have confirmed Western doubts about the battlefield viability of the Mi-24 'Hind' gunship models, for while this new machine is clearly derived from earlier Mil helicopters (including the dynamic system of the Mi-24 driving a new five-blade articulated main rotor), it adopted the US practice of a much slimmer and smaller fuselage for increased manoeuvrability and reduced vulnerability over the modern high-technology battlefield.

The Mi-28 thus bears a passing resemblance to the AH-64A Apache in US Army service, and among its operational features are IR suppression of the

The smallest of current battlefield helicopters, the Agusta A 129 Mangusta (mongoose) is fast and agile, but possesses no gun armament and carries the optronic sensors for its flight and fire-control systems on a steerable platform low on the nose. The weapons load is supported by the four hardpoints under the stub wing, and is here represented by two multi-tube launchers for unguided rockets, and two superimposed pairs of twin launchers for BGM-71 TOW heavyweight anti-tank missiles.

podded engines' exhausts, IR decoys, upgraded steel/titanium armour, optronic sighting and targeting systems for use in conjunction with the undernose 30mm cannon and disposable weapons (including AAMs) carried on the stub wing hardpoints, and millimetric-wavelength radar.

The type clearly possesses an air-combat capability against other battlefield helicopters, and other notable features include a far higher level of survivability and the provision of a small compartment on the left-hand side of the fuselage, probably for the rescue of downed aircrew.

In 1992 the Russians revealed that the type had been developed in competition with the Kamov V-80 (later Ka-50), and that the latter had been selected for Russian service as the Ka-50. Mil then offered the Mi-28 on the export market, with a view to placing the type in production should an order materialise, but in 1993 it was announced that the type is in fact to be procured for Russian service alongside the Ka-50, always providing that adequate financing can be assured.

Due to fly in 1996 for a possible service debut in the late 1990s, the Mi-28N 'Havoc-B' is a night and adverse-weather derivative of the baseline Mi-28, with a specialised nav/attack system including a mast-mounted sight incorporating the antenna for millimetric-wavelength radar, FLIR and a low-light-level TV.

The other three helicopter gunship types currently flying are the Agusta A 129 Mangusta from Italy, the Atlas CSH-2 Rooivalk from South Africa, and the Eurocopter Tigre/Tiger from France and Germany.

The first tandem-seat anti-tank helicopter developed in Europe, the A 129 Mangusta offers good performance, powerful anti-tank armament and associated sights, and a small fuselage profile featuring vertically staggered tandem seating for the gunner and pilot, the latter seated above and behind the former. The type was designed in response to a 1972 Italian army requirement, and the first of five prototype and development helicopters flew in September 1983, an exhaustive development programme then being undertaken before the Mangusta entered service in October 1990 with full day and night offensive capability. The Integrated Multiplex System monitors the helicopter and all its systems via two computers, leaving the two crew members to devote their attention to the mission. The standard A 129 has provision for the retrofit of a mast-mounted sight system, and the manufacturer has also proposed a shipborne model able to undertake the anti-ship or close-support roles, the former with an armament of two Sea Killer Mk 2 or four Sea Skua missiles supported by appropriate search/designation radar, and the latter with an armament of AGM-65 Maverick ASMs in addition to the A 129's standard TOW and rocket fit.

Revealed as the XH-2 prototype that first flew in February 1990, the CSH-2 Rooivalk was designed as South Africa's standard battlefield helicopter in light of its forces' combat experience in Namibia during the 1980s. The type was evolved from the Aérospatiale SA.330 Puma with a locally upgraded version of a French turboshaft, the Turbomeca Makila IA2, and represents the conclusion of South Africa's evolutionary programme of battlefield helicopter development via the Alpha XH-1 and Beta XTP-1. The XH-1 was a gunship demonstrator combining the dynamic system of the Aérospatiale Alouette III with a new fuselage and an advanced weapon system; the crew of two was seated in tandem in upward-staggered separate cockpits, and the gun armament comprised one 20mm GA1 cannon with 1,000 rounds in a servo-actuated mounting under the fuselage. The XTP-1 subsystems flight-test platform was evolved in similar fashion as a radical development of the SA.330 Puma. Designed from 1984, the CSH-2 has the Rattler cannon system (with a 20mm GA1 Cobra gun in a servo-operated chin turret fed from a magazine in the hold and operated in conjunction with a helmet sight worn by the co-pilot/gunner), and a variety of disposable loads on the six hardpoints under the two new stub wings (produced as a single unit passing through the erstwhile passenger cabin). The political situation in southern Africa has eased to the point at which the South African forces no longer need the Rooivalk in substantial numbers, although 16 of the type are being procured for the equipment of two squadrons from 1998, so the type's commercial success probably depends on export orders. In the early 1990s, Atlas was involved in discussions with possible co-production partners in the Middle East and South America. In 1995 it was announced that Malaysia is considering a purchase of the type.

The Tigre/Tiger single-rotor helicopter was planned to meet French and West German requirements for an advanced multi-role type for battlefield operations in the typical European scenario, and originated from a 1984 memorandum of understanding. The original development was halted in 1986 because of rapidly escalating costs, but was relaunched during 1987 in basically common French and West German anti-tank models and as a French escort model. The airframe is built largely of composite materials, and the first of five development helicopters flew in April 1991. The Tigre is planned in two forms for the French army. The first of these is the Hélicoptère Anti-Char (HAR), or anti-tank helicopter, of which 100 (originally 140) are required. The primary armament is planned as a maximum of eight anti-tank missiles (all HOT 2 or Trigat weapons or four of each type, all aimed via the Osiris mast-mounted sight) on the inner underwing hardpoints and four Matra Mistral short-range AAMs on the outer underwing hardpoints. The Osiris system combines a TV, FLIR and laser ranger for the weapon system operator, while the pilot uses a nose-mounted FLIR as his primary night vision sensor. The Hélicoptère d'Appui et de Protection (HAP), or attack and protection helicopter, is required to the extent of 115 (originally 75). This model carries a chin-mounted 30mm GIAT 30/781B cannon with between 150 and 450 rounds of ammunition and, on the underwing hardpoints, two multiple launchers each carrying twenty-two 2.68in (68mm) unguided rockets and either four Matra Mistral short-range AAMs or two multiple launchers each carrying twelve 2.68in unguided rockets. The sensors of this variant include a roof-mounted combination of TV and FLIR optics, direct optics and a laser ranger. Originally ordered as the PAC-2 second-generation anti-tank helicopter, the Tiger is now the UHU support for the German army, which requires 212 such machines. The model is basically similar to the HAC apart from its ability to carry Stinger 2 short-range AAMs on the outboard underwing hardpoints in place of the French variant's Mistral weapons. In common with France, Germany was reviewing the nature and extent of the programme during the early 1990s, the driving forces being rising development and procurement costs as well as the decline (or rather demise) of the Warsaw Pact threat that this battlefield helicopter was intended to tackle.

113

Multi-Role Versatility

THE cost of developing, building and operating aircraft as complex and advanced as modern helicopters has always placed a premium on helicopter versatility, so that any type can undertake as many roles as possible. This tendency has increased in recent years, especially with the collapse of the USSR and thus its end as a credible threat to the West, and as part of the resulting 'peace dividend' there has been further pressure for any new helicopter type to offer multiple capabilities on the basis of a common airframe/dynamic system combination.

Such a tendency had been obvious from the beginning of the helicopter's operational use, of course, as evidenced by the employment of the early Sikorsky and Bell helicopters for the observation, training, liaison, observation and casevac roles, and then taken to a more advanced level with the advent of more capable helicopters such as the Sikorsky S-58 that was delivered in general transport, assault landing and naval variants (the last in complementary anti-submarine hunter and killer pairs with specialised avionics and weapons respectively). The advent of the turboshaft further increased this tendency by improving the helicopter's all-round payload/range capabilities, and thus even small helicopters such as the Aérospatiale Alouette series could be configured for armed tasks (over both land and sea battlefields) as an alternative to its baseline transport and communications roles. Further development of the turboshaft-powered helicopter resulted in machines that were more fully optimised for their roles, especially in features such as

The Boeing CH-47 Chinook is the most important medium/heavy-lift transport helicopter available to Western-oriented nations, and has undergone a long programme of development as well as construction so that modern helicopters of the same basic type offer considerably more sophisticated capabilities as well as superior performance to the initial CH-47A helicopters that made their operational debut in the Vietnam War.

the mission package (avionics and weapons) and landing gear optimised for land and shipborne use (twin skid and wheeled tricycle respectively).

A classic example of this tendency is provided by a British type, the small but extremely versatile Westland Lynx that was planned from the beginning in closely related military and naval variants. The Lynx was designed from 1968 within the context of an Anglo-French agreement for the collaborative development of three tactical helicopters. Design leadership of two was allocated to France (the Aérospatiale SA.330 Puma and Aérospatiale SA.341 Gazelle) and of the third to the UK (the WG.13 design that matured as the Lynx multi-role type for land-based and shipborne use).

The WG.13 was designed as an all-metal type based on a pod-and-boom fuselage accommodating the flightcrew of one or two at the front, each crew member having his own jettisonable door. This left the major part of the pod section for the payload-carrying hold section, whose dimensions from the back of the pilots' seats include a length of 6ft 9in (2.06m), width of 5ft 10in (1.78m) and height of 4ft 8in (1.42m); the hold is accessed by two sliding and jettisonable doors. The boom extends rearward from the upper part of the pod section's rear face, and supports the anti-torque rotor. The helicopter was made as compact as possible to facilitate operations from small naval platforms such as frigates, but very careful design ensured that the hold was large enough to carry an infantry squad or other suitable load in the type's land-based variants. For full optimisation in the land-based and shipborne roles, provision was made for two types of landing gear, in the form of a fixed tricycle arrangement for the naval model and a twin-skid arrangement for the land-based model.

It was also decided from the start of the programme that high performance and great agility were essential prerequisites for naval and military success, and an advanced rotor system was designed. This was based on four-blade main and tail rotors, the main rotor being of the semi-rigid type with each blade attached to the rotor hub by titanium plates and a root arm. Power was provided by two 900hp (671kW) Rolls-Royce Gem Mk 2 turboshafts located side-by-side over the pod/boom junction and driving a gearbox between themselves and the main rotor.

The first of 13 prototypes flew in March 1971, and development centred on two streams for the land-optimised variant with skid landing gear and the

Top and above: The naval version of the Westland Lynx, identifiable by its tricycle rather than twin-skid landing gear, is a notably compact helicopter than can nonetheless carry a useful payload (men or equipment in its secondary transport role, or electronics and weapons in its primary anti-submarine and anti-ship role) and offers very high performance as well as considerable agility and excellent reliability.

ship-optimised variant with tricycle landing gear. The prototype of the baseline land-based Lynx AH.Mk 1 model first flew in April 1972, and the type entered service in 1977. Some 113 helicopters were built to this standard, which offers better performance than the naval Lynx as it has the same basic powerplant but a lower empty weight. Apart from the twin-skid landing gear, this model's major differences from the naval Lynx are a slightly longer fuselage and a different combination of avionics and weapons. The Lynx has been qualified for a wide assortment of weapons, but in its basic anti-tank role with the British army the Lynx AH.Mk 1 carries container-launchers for eight BGM-71 TOW heavyweight anti-tank missiles guided with the aid of an M65 stabilized roof-mounted sight. The cabin can accommodate reload TOW missiles, or up to 10 troops, or a Milan ground-launched anti-tank missile crew with launcher, missiles and other equipment, or casualties, or freight.

The Lynx AH.Mk 5 designation is applied to three examples of an improved version of the Lynx AH.Mk 1, with two 1,120hp (835kW) Gem Mk 41-1 turboshafts later upgraded to 1,135hp (846kW) Gem Mk 42-1 standard, and a maximum disposable ordnance load of about 1,210lb (549kg).

The Lynx AH.Mk 7 designation is applied to 11 examples of a further-improved model for the British army, with upgraded systems, Gem Mk 42-1 turboshafts, swept-tip BERP main rotor blades of composite construction (retrofitted as the original metal blades were withdrawn), and a tail rotor rotating in the opposite direction to that of the Lynx AH.Mk 1 for a greater maximum take-off weight. All surviving Lynx AH.Mk 1 helicopters are being upgraded via the Lynx AH.Mk 1GT interim standard (uprated engines and rotors) to this definitive standard, which also includes the thermal imaging TOW (TITOW) anti-tank missile sight system, which is the standard M65 unit fitted with a GEC Sensors thermal imaging sensor for improved nocturnal capability; the complete package offers better low-level hovering and manoeuvring capabilities, facilitating nap-of-the-earth anti-tank operations, and protection from IR-homing missiles is improved by the use of large hot gas/cool freestream air mixers fitted over the turboshaft exhausts.

The Lynx AH.Mk 9 designation is applied to 16 new-build examples and eight Lynx AH.Mk 7 conversions to an updated Lynx AH.Mk 7 unarmed mobile command post and tactical transport standard with upgraded avionics, BERP rotor blades of composite construction, an upgraded gearbox, Gem Mk 42-1 turboshafts, tricycle landing gear, secure radio equipment, an improved identification friend or foe (IFF) facility, a Decca Tactical Air Navigation System, a cockpit voice recorder, a tele-briefing system, and a maximum take-off weight increased by 550lb (249kg).

Developed as a private venture, the Battlefield Lynx is an armed version with a roof-mounted sight and provision for eight BGM-71 TOW anti-tank missiles. Westland is also offering a Battlefield Lynx 800 version of this helicopter with a powerplant of two 1,350hp (1,007kW) LHTEC

(Allison/Garrett) T800 turboshafts for improved hot-and-high performance. A variant that has yet to secure any production order, the Lynx-3 is a much improved dedicated anti-tank development with a powerplant of two 1,346hp (1,004kW) Gem Mk 60 turboshafts, an advanced-technology main rotor, and a slightly lengthened fuselage housing two pilots and a deployable anti-tank missile team, the missile team's reloads, and pylon-mounted weapons such as Hellfire, HOT or TOW anti-tank missiles, and provision for FIM-92A Stinger or Shorts Starstreak lightweight AAMs.

The Lynx HAS.Mk 2 is the baseline naval model of the Lynx family, and is an advanced anti-submarine and anti-ship helicopter suitable for deployment on small surface vessels. The Lynx HAS.Mk 2 prototype first flew in May 1972, and the variant entered service from December 1977. Production totalled 60 helicopters, and the type is distinguishable from its land-based counterpart by its fixed but castoring tricycle landing gear, its folding tail, and its combination of naval avionics and weapons. As alternatives to its primary roles, the Lynx HAS.Mk 2 can be used for transport (with a payload of 10 troops, or 2,000lb/907kg of freight carried internally or 3,000lb/1,361kg of freight carried externally), or underway replenishment of ships at sea, or SAR.

The Lynx Mk 2(FN) designation is applied to 26 of the Lynx HAS.Mk 2 version for the French navy, with a revised suite of electronics and operational equipment.

The Lynx HAS.Mk 3 designation is applied to 23 of an improved British naval model delivered between March 1982 and March 1985 with a powerplant of two 1,120hp (835kW) Gem Mk 41-1 turboshafts, and supplemented by 53 Lynx HAS.Mk 2s upgraded to the same higher-performance standard. Between November 1987 and November 1988, another seven helicopters were delivered to the improved Lynx HAS.Mk 3S standard with secure radio and an upgraded ESM system, and this number was increased by 23 Lynx HAS.Mk 2 helicopters converted to the same standard. The latest subvariant is the Lynx HAS.Mk 3CTS, a designation applied to seven helicopters upgraded with the Lynx HAS.Mk 8's Racal RAMS 4000 Central Tactical System (CTS).

The Lynx Mk 4(FN) is the designation applied to 14 of the Lynx HAS.Mk 3 version for the French navy, with the same equipment as the Lynx Mk 2(FN).

The Lynx HAS.Mk 8 is the latest anti-ship and anti-submarine development in the naval Lynx series, a standard to which 65 helicopters of the Lynx HAS.Mk 3 series are being upgraded with improvements such as a better tail rotor turning in the opposite direction to that of earlier models, composite-structure BERP main rotor blades, and an electronic system featuring an upgraded ESM system (the Racal RNS252 'Super TANS' navigation system with GPS input, and the Racal RAMS 4000 CTS with all tactical data processed for display on a multi-function CRT). It had originally been planned to fit 360-degree scan radar (the GEC Ferranti Seaspray Mk 3 and Thorn EMI Super Searcher had been shortlisted) with its antenna in a

Top and above: The latest land-based version of the Westland Lynx has adopted the type of tricycle landing gear arrangement initially developed for the naval model. In its battlefield role the land-based Lynx can be fitted with an assortment of weapons including medium- and heavy-weight anti-tank missiles, and can also be used for the transport of specialised anti-tank teams with their ground-based firing unit plus a considerable number of reload missiles.

chin-mounted radome, but the installation of such a radar has been abandoned for financial reasons. The final electronic fit thus includes the original Seaspray Mk 1 radar, relocated to a chin radome, to leave the nose position clear for the GEC Sensors Sea Owl Passive Identification Device (PID), which is a long-range thermal imaging system. In other respects, the Lynx HAS.Mk 8 differs from the Lynx HAS.Mk 2 in details such as its powerplant of two 1,135hp (846kW) Rolls-Royce Gem Mk 42-1 turboshafts.

The naval version of the Lynx has also been widely exported in a number of Lynx Mk 20, Lynx Mk 80 and Lynx Mk 90 variants, and Westland is offering the Super Lynx version of the Lynx HAS.Mk 8 variant for export, with 360-degree scan GEC Ferranti Seaspray Mk 3 radar and a powerplant of two Gem Mk 42-1 turboshafts as standard, plus provision for customer options such as dunking sonar, Sea Skua or Penguin anti-ship missiles, Stingray torpedoes and the main and tail rotor developments of the Lynx AH.Mk 7/Lynx HAS.Mk 8 series.

Of the two French helicopters that were developed and placed in production within the context of the Anglo-French agreement mentioned above, the larger is the Aérospatiale Puma that has been extensively developed by the parent company (now Eurocopter France) through three main generations, and with a bewildering number of designation and name changes. Having made extensive use of helicopters in their Far Eastern and North African operations of the 1950s and early 1960s, the French were well placed to assess the capabilities of current tactical helicopters and thereby arrive at the right specification for an effective successor type. In the medium transport role, it was clear that helicopters such as the Sikorsky S-58 (CH-34 series) were limited in utility by their piston-engined powerplants, which were bulky, offered only a comparatively low power-to-weight ratio, and required the type of fuel and maintenance that would both become increasingly scarce as more operators switched to turbine engines. The low power-to-weight ratio of the powerplant meant that payload was fairly limited, and that it was impossible to outfit such tactical helicopters with the full instrumentation that would have provided them with an effective night and all-weather capability.

In 1962, therefore, the French army issued a requirement for a new tactical transport able to operate under all weather conditions, and in 1963 Sud-Aviation began work on the new type under the designation SA.330. The company already had extensive experience in turbine-powered helicopter design with its Alouette series, and its Super Frelon provided data on the design of large transport helicopters. What the company now planned was a helicopter mid-way between the Alouette and Super Frelon in size, with a pod-and-boom fuselage, retractable tricycle landing gear for higher speed, and a powerplant of two turboshafts located above the cabin roof as the core of a dynamic system also including a four-blade main rotor and a five-blade tail rotor.

The twin-engined powerplant offered great reliability and the turboshaft engines provided both a low vibration level and a high power-to-weight ratio, thereby reducing the fatigue experienced by the helicopter's occupants and maximising the helicopter's payload. The cabin was 15ft 4in (4.68m) long, 5ft 8in (1.73m) wide and 4ft 11in (1.50m) high, with access provided by a large sliding door on each side.

The first of two SA.330A prototypes flew in April 1965, and there followed six pre-production helicopters before the SA.330B initial production version entered service in March 1969, with a powerplant of two 1,328hp (990kW) Turmo IIIC4 turboshafts for the carriage of a 6,614lb (3,000kg) payload. The type was built to the extent of 145 helicopters for the French army, proving

Top: The Royal Navy's Westland Lynx HAS.Mk 8 is a development of the Super Lynx concept with the nose extensively modified for installation of the GEC-Marconi Sea Owl thermal imaging system in a trainable turret on a platform above the repositioned Ferranti Seaspray Mk I search radar that provides target data for the BAe Sea Skua missile that is the helicopter's primary weapon for use against light and medium surface vessels.

Above: The Lynx AH.Mk 9 is the British army's version of the Battlefield Lynx, the land-based equivalent of the Super Lynx naval helicopter with an uprated powerplant, more advanced rotor blades, and more capable electronics. This machine is equipped with container launchers for eight HOT anti-tank missiles.

highly successful in its intended role and thus paving the way for substantial export orders for military and naval models. The SA.330C Puma was developed in parallel with the SA.330B as the baseline export version with a powerplant of two 1,402hp (1,045kW) Turmo IVC turboshafts.

The British had recognised the potential of the SA.330 from an early date, and in 1967 the type was selected as the last of the trio of helicopters for joint British and French manufacture (the other two being the Sud-Aviation SA.341 Gazelle and the Westland Lynx). The British saw the type as a supplement and replacement respectively for its Westland Wessex HC.Mk 2 and Westland Whirlwind helicopters. The resulting SA.330E made its maiden flight in November 1970, and the first of an eventual 48 helicopters (plus a number of attrition replacements) was delivered to the RAF during January 1971, for service with the British designation Puma HC.Mk 1.

The SA.330H is an uprated military version of the SA.330C, with a powerplant of two 1,576hp (1,175kW) Turmo IVC turboshafts for a higher maximum take-off weight. The SA.330L is a further improved export model with Turmo IVC turboshafts, inlet de-icing, and rotor blades of composite (fibreglass) rather than steel/light alloy structure. Among the operators of the type is South Africa, which during the early 1990s was evaluating a conversion for the battlefield role with a sensor/armament fit derived from that of the Atlas Rooivalk: a large stub wing carries two wingtip missile stations and four underwing hardpoints, the former for a pair of Armscor V3/Darter IR-homing AAMs and the latter for pods each containing four Atlas Swift laser-homing anti-tank missiles; the laser-designating equipment for the Swifts is carried in a substantial nose-mounted box.

The Puma has also been built under licence and further developed in countries such as Romania, with the local designation IAR-330, a powerplant of two 1,575hp (1,175kW) Turbomecanica (Turbomeca) Turmo IVC turboshafts and, in some helicopters, a considerably heavier armament; and South Africa, with the local designation Atlas Oryx (originally Gemsbok) as a hybrid combining the airframe of the SA.330 with the dynamic system of the AS.332 Super Puma for enhanced weight-lifting capability under hot-and-high conditions.

The AS.332 Super Puma is the second-generation derivative of the SA.330, designed to prolong the useful life of the basic SA.330 into the early part of the next century. In 1974, Aérospatiale began the process of developing the AS.332 as a much-redesigned and improved Puma with many detail changes (including revised landing gear able to absorb higher-rate landings and designed to 'kneel' for easier access to the larger cabin), in addition to an uprated powerplant of two 1,789hp (1,327kW) Turbomeca Makila IA turboshafts for greater performance even with a heavier payload (which could include 21 rather than 18 troops in a cabin 19ft 10.5in (6.05m) long, 5ft 10.75in (1.80m) wide and 5ft 1in (1.55m) high). Other changes were incorporated to reduce cabin noise, maintenance requirements and operational vulnerability.

The AS.331 prototype flew in September 1977 to test the revised dynamic system, and the first of six AS.332 prototypes made its initial flight during September 1978, a successful flight test and development programme allowing deliveries to begin in mid-1981. Since that time the helicopter has secured a useful rate of sales to operators who appreciate the type's low-maintenance but damage-resistant composite rotor blades and other tactically desirable features. The main subvariant is the AS.332B-1 with upgraded engines for better hot-and-high performance; since the January 1992 merger of Aérospatiale's and MBB's helicopter interests to create Eurocopter, the AS.332B has been designated as the AS.532UC Cougar.

Offsetting Helicopter Development and Production Costs

THE cost of developing and producing any modern weapon, even before the type has entered full service and started to accrue operating and other life-cycle expenses, is very considerable. Moreover, the cost of developing and launching production of a modern weapon seems to increase geometrically whereas improvement in the weapons' capabilities seems to increase arithmetically. For this reason, therefore, there has been a tendency since the 1960s for the development of modern military aircraft, of both the fixed- and rotary-wing types, to be undertaken on a collaborative international basis. The additional administrative burden of such programmes certainly increases the overall cost to a certain degree, but the division of this cost and the promise of larger overall production totals is generally thought to yield an overall reduction in development and production cost even if, as is generally the case, there is a production line in each of the participating nations. Fixed-wing aircraft resulting from such programmes include the SEPECAT Jaguar, Panavia Tornado, Eurofighter EFA and SOKO J-22 Orao/CNIAR IAR-93, and rotary-wing machines now include the European Helicopter Industries EH.101 and Eurocopter Tiger/Tigre. There are many countries that lack the financial resources and technological skills to enter into such a collaborative programme except on terms of inequality with the major partner(s), and it suits such countries to become involved in a programme to build the warplane under licence, starting with assembly of machines delivered as kits of knocked-down major components and progressing to manufacture of the complete weapon with an increasingly large indigenous input. This keeps an increasingly large part of the production cost from moving to a foreign nation, and in the case of more advanced aircraft allows the licensee industry to develop its technological capabilities to the point at which it can begin to consider collaborative ventures in the future.

The AS.332F is the naval counterpart of the AS.332B with a folding tail, a deck landing-assistance device for enhanced ship compatibility under adverse weather and sea conditions, improved anti-corrosion protection, and provision for nose-mounted radar. The model is suitable for the SAR role with Bendix RDR-1400, RCA Primus 40/50 or Honeywell (RCA) Primus 500 radar; or the anti-submarine role with Thomson-CSF Varan radar, Alcatel HS 12 or Alcatel/Thomson-Sintra HS 312 dunking sonar and two Mk 46 torpedoes; or the anti-ship role with Omera-Segid Héraclès ORB 3214 radar and a missile armament of two heavyweight AM.39 Exocets, or six lightweight AS.15TTs, or one Exocet and three AS.15TTs; use of the AS.15TT requires the installation of Thomson-CSF Agrion-15 radar in place of the ORB 3214. The current variant is the AS.332F-1 with the improved powerplant of two Makila IA1 turboshafts and provision for two AM.39 Exocet anti-ship missiles, and since the creation of Eurocopter, the AS.332F-1 has been redesignated as the AS.532MC Cougar for the unarmed SAR role, or as the AS.532SC Cougar for the armed anti-submarine/ship role.

The AS.332M is the upgraded version of the AS.332B, with the cabin lengthened by 2ft 6in (0.76m) to 22ft 4in (6.81m) for the carriage of 25 troops, and more fuel for increased range despite the heavier payload. The current variant is the AS.332M-1 with a powerplant of two Makila IA1 turboshafts for unimpaired hot-and-high operations with 25 fully equipped troops, and since the creation of Eurocopter, this variant has been designated as the AS.532UL Cougar.

The AS.532UL Hélicoptère d'Observation Radar et d'Investigation sur Zone, or radar observation and zone surveillance helicopter (HORIZON) is the battlefield surveillance model of which France ordered four examples for delivery from 1995. The origins of the type can be traced to the evaluation from 1986 of an SA.330 with the small Orchée radar using an antenna arranged to fold down from the lower rear part of the fuselage's pod section, and success with this initial development model paved the way for the AS.532 with the larger Orchidée pulse-Doppler radar able to provide 360-degree coverage out to a radius of 93 miles (150km) from a hovering altitude of 9,845ft (3,000m). The radar antenna was located ventrally under the rear of the payload hold on a hinged arm that allowed it to be swung 90 degrees to the rear (under the boom) when not in use, and the radar was linked to its Mistrigri ground station by an Agatha data link. The type was also to be fitted with the Matra Saphir chaff/flare dispenser, a type capable of manual or semi-automatic operation, the latter requiring the installation of an RWR. In 1990 the type was cancelled for financial reasons, but the prototype's excellent performance during the 1991 Gulf War, when it was operated without a data link in the downgraded HORIZON form, led to a review of this decision, and as a result the French army has been permitted to place an initial order, scaled-down from the original requirement for 20 systems based on the larger AS.532 Cougar Mk II.

The IPTN NAS-322 is the version of the AS.332B-1 built under licence in Indonesia, and similar types have also been assembled in Singapore and Spain from kits of French-supplied components.

The AS.332 Super Puma Mk II is the third-generation development of the SA.300 family, and is a much improved Super Puma variant with upgraded electronics and systems, a higher-rated power train, an advanced main rotor with lengthened blades terminating in parabolic tips, and with the rear fuselage lengthened by 1ft 5.75in (0.45m) to provide clearance between the larger main rotor and the tail rotor. The first Super Puma Mk II flew in February 1987 and displayed improved performance and manoeuvrability as well as superior hot-and-high capability. The type entered service in 1993 and, since the establishment of Eurocopter, has been offered as the AS.532 Cougar Mk II whose two basic subvariants are the unarmed AS.532U2 Cougar Mk II and armed AS.532A2 Cougar Mk II.

The smaller of the two French helicopters included in the Anglo-French agreement mentioned above is the Aérospatiale Gazelle. The origins of this dainty type can be found in the realisation by Sud-Aviation that, although it had enjoyed great technical and commercial success with its Alouette II and Alouette III series of utility light helicopters, the decline in orders for these two types in the early 1960s indicated the onset of obsolescence, and that a successor type was needed to maintain the company's position as pre-eminent European manufacturer of light helicopters. The company used the proven capabilities of the Alouette III as a starting point, and decided that the new helicopter's most important improvements over the Alouette III should lie in the fields of speed and manoeuvrability. Additional speed should be made possible by the adoption of the Oredon engine, one of the new turboshaft engines then being designed by Turbomeca, and greater agility was promised by developments in the rotor head and rotor blade design.

A key factor was the company's July 1964 agreement with MBB of West Germany for the collaborative development of a glassfibre rotor blade and the semi-rigid rotor system to use this blade. In prospect, therefore, were greater speed, enhanced manoeuvrability, reduced weight and simplified maintenance. Another driving force was the British army's 1965 selection of the Sud-Aviation X-300 project as replacement for its fleet of Westland (Saro) Skeeter and Westland (Agusta-Bell) Sioux light helicopters, and in 1967 the British and French governments signed an agreement for the collaborative development and production of one British and two French helicopters, respectively the Westland Lynx and the Sud-Aviation SA.340 Gazelle and SA.330 Puma.

The SA.340 inherited the rigid rotor design of the X-300 project, but had to adopt a different engine as Turbomeca had abandoned development of the Oredon turboshaft. The selected engine was the same manufacturer's well-proved Astazou, and the first SA.340 prototype flew in April 1967 with a 362hp (270kW) Astazou II turboshaft driving conventional main and tail rotors. The second SA.340 prototype flew 12 months later and was typical of the planned production standard with a rigid main rotor and a *fenestron* shrouded anti-torque rotor set into the T-tail. Some directional instability was encountered as a result of distortion in the glassfibre fin, but this was cured by moving the tailplane to the low-set position and fitting it with small endplate fins. Efforts to cure the main rotor's tendency to stall, vibrate and pitch at high speed were less successful, and it was found that the problem lay with the use of rigid blades in a three-blade installation. The third helicopter was therefore completed to SA.341 standard with a semi-articulated rotor head, and this performed well. Another three SA.341 pre-production prototypes followed, and the SA.341's success seemed assured by several world records. The type was named Gazelle in July 1969, and the French manufacturer became Aérospatiale when Sud-Aviation and Nord-Aviation were amalgamated in January 1971.

The first SA.341 from the production line was completed in August 1971, but ran into severe transmission vibration and ground resonance problems on its first flight: the design team had successfully tested a number of improvements such as a longer cabin, an additional door, a larger tail unit, and the 590hp (440kW) Astazou IIIA turboshaft on an individual basis, but in concert they had created problems that took more than a year to solve.

The type entered production at much the same time in France and the UK, the latter's first model being the SA.341B (212 helicopters) that entered service as the British army's Gazelle AH.Mk 1 with a powerplant of one 590hp (440kW) Astazou IIIN turboshaft. The SA.341C is the Royal Navy's Gazelle HT.Mk 2 trainer of which 40 were delivered; the SA.341D is the RAF's Gazelle HT.Mk 3 trainer of which 29 were delivered; and the SA.341E is the RAF's Gazelle HCC.Mk 4 communications type of which just one was delivered but was later supplemented by three Gazelle HT.Mk 3 conversions.

The SA.341F is the initial French army version that entered service as partial replacement for the SA.318 Alouette II in the observation and liaison roles, and 170 were built with a powerplant of one Astazou IIIC turboshaft. Some 110 were later converted to SA.341M anti-tank standard with a roof-mounted sight and outrigger pylons for HOT missiles, redeliveries beginning in September 1978, and most of the others were adapted to SA.341F/Canon interim escort and gunship standard with a 20mm M621 cannon on the starboard side of the cabin. There is also a reconnaissance version with a simplified version of the Athos magnifying sight used on the HOT-armed SA.342M variant.

The SA.341H is the SA.341B/F export version with the Astazou IIIB turboshaft, and was built under licence in Yugoslavia as the SOKO SA.341H Partizan liaison and reconnaissance helicopter. In the armed reconnaissance role, the Yugoslav variant carries an armament of four AT-2 'Swatter' or AT-3 'Sagger' wire-guided anti-tank missiles and two examples of the air-to-air version of the SA-7 'Grail' shoulder-launched SAM.

The SA.342 is the variant of the SA.341, with an uprated powerplant of one 872hp (650kW) Turbomeca Astazou XIV turboshaft for greater performance and payload, especially under hot-and-high conditions. The type first flew in prototype form during May 1973, and entered production during 1976 as the SA.342J civil helicopter that was delivered from 1977, before being complemented for export by the SA.342K with the Astazou XIVH turboshaft fitted with momentum-separation shrouds over the inlet.

The SA.342L is the baseline military version of the SA. 342J civil helicopter, with an improved *fenestron* shrouded tail rotor and a number of detail modifications. The type has also been built under licence in Yugoslavia as the SOKO SA.342 HERA special-purpose and SA.342 GAMA gunship models. The current subvariant is the SA.342L-1 with a powerplant of one 858hp (640kW) Astazou XIVM turboshaft.

Although this looks like an S-61 that served with the US forces under the core designation H-3 and US Navy name Sea King, it is in fact a Sikorsky S-62 as indicated by the centrally located inlet for its single turboshaft engine. This was the company's first amphibious helicopter, and was first flown in May 1958 with the three-blade main rotor of the piston-engined S-55 helicopter. The type entered production as the S-62A and was later improved to S-62B standard with the four-blade main rotor of the piston-engined S-58 reduced to the same 53ft 0in (16.16m) diameter as the rotor of the S-62A. The example shown here is an HH-52A search-and-rescue version of the S-62B for the US Coast Guard.

The Sikorsky S-70 series, which serves the US forces with the core designation S-60, is a true multi-role type. The S-70 was planned in successful competition with a Boeing type as the Utility Tactical Transport Aircraft System replacement for the Bell Models 204 and 205 (UH-1 Iroquois or 'Huey'), and has since been built in large numbers for an apparently endless string of roles varying from combat-search-and-rescue to VIP transport via tactical transport, Special Forces infiltration and exfiltration, electronic warfare and casualty evacuation.

The SA.342M is the dedicated anti-tank version of the SA.342L-1 for the French army, with the SFIM APX-Bezu M397 Athos gyro-stabilized sight for the guidance of four or six HOT anti-tank missiles in two twin or triple installations, although the type can alternatively be armed with two 0.3in (7.62mm) machine gun pods or one 20mm M621 cannon (in the latter case being designated SA.342M/Canon Gazelle). Deliveries began in June 1980, and other modifications comprise an autopilot and an exhaust deflector for reduced vulnerability to IR-homing SAMs. All armed Gazelles are being fitted with the SFIM Divine night/adverse-weather thermal sight for HOT missiles to create the SA.342M Viviane Gazelle or, in the case of 70 helicopters, with the T2000 sight and provision for four Mistral short-range AAMs to create the SA.342M ATAM Gazelle for the escort role.

The French manufacturer, in either its original Aérospatiale or current Eurocopter France guises, has also produced a number of other light helicopters that have been adapted for the military roles, the most important being the Ecureuil and Dauphin series that are now known in their military forms as the Fennec and Panther. Of these, the larger and more capable is the Dauphin/Panther. Developed as successor to the SA.319 Alouette III series, the SA.360 Dauphin first flew in prototype form during June 1972 as a trim helicopter with a powerplant of one 1,050hp (783kW) Turbomeca Astazou XVIIIA turboshaft driving a four-blade main rotor and a *fenestron* shrouded tail rotor, and with accommodation for a crew of two plus up to 10 passengers, or four litters and a medical attendant, or freight. Only limited military sales were achieved, largely for use in the communications role, and although an SA.361H anti-tank/assault transport was developed as a private venture, Aérospatiale soon appreciated that both military and civil applications would be better served by a twin-engined powerplant.

The initial twin-engine version was the SA.365C Dauphin 2, flown in prototype form during January 1975 with a powerplant of two Turbomeca Arriel turboshafts. There was considerably greater sales interest in this model, which entered production later in the decade with a powerplant of two 660hp (492kW) Arriel IA turboshafts or, in the improved SA.365N Dauphin 2 version, two 710hp (529kW) Arriel IC turboshafts. The SA.365N introduced a large degree of composite construction as well as retractable

One of the practices used when a helicopter cannot land to disgorge its load of embarked troops is for the troops to use the rapelling technique to descend ropes reaching to the ground through obstacles such as trees.

landing gear, and the SA.365F Dauphin 2 is the versatile naval development of the SA.365N intended primarily for the anti-ship role with Agrion-15 search radar, MAD with a towed 'bird', an armament of two or four AS.15TT short-range anti-ship missiles, and the avionics for mid-course targeting update of ship-launched Otomat long-range anti-ship missiles. The type is also available in SAR configuration with search radar, a rescue winch, an automatic navigation system, and a hover/transition coupler.

The manufacturer also offers a more advanced anti-submarine capability in a derivative with Thomson-Sintra (Alcatel) ASM HS 312 dunking sonar, Sextant Avionique (Crouzet) DHAX 3 MAD, and an armament of two lightweight homing torpedoes.

The creation of Eurocopter led to the redesignation of the military version of the SA.365 Dauphin 2 as the AS.565 Panther, which is now offered in the unarmed AS.565MA SAR and sea surveillance model, and the armed AS.565SA anti-ship and anti-submarine model.

First flown in February 1984, and now known as the AS.565 Panther, the AS.365M Dauphin 2 is the dedicated military version of the SA.365N series with greater use of composite materials, a longer fuselage fitted with armoured seats, cable cutters for safer low-altitude flight capability, a strengthened cabin floor and landing gear, sliding rather than hinged doors, crash-resistant fuel tanks, IR-reducing exhausts, and the use of composite materials and special paints to reduce electromagnetic and thermal signatures. The AS.565AA Panther is the armed subvariant with two lateral outriggers, each with a single hardpoint for the carriage of two multiple launchers for unguided rockets (either twenty-two 2.68in/68mm Thomson-Brandt or nineteen 2.75in/70mm Forges de

Zeebrugge weapons), or two pods each carrying one 20mm GIAT M621 cannon with 180 rounds, or four two-round packs of Matra Mistral short-range AAMs. The AS.565CA Panther is the anti-tank subvariant capable of carrying two quadruple launch units for HOT missiles, aimed via a Viviane day/night unit for an SFIM gyro-stabilized platform holding a TRT Hector IR camera and SAT deviation-measuring equipment. The AS. 565UA Panther is the unarmed utility subvariant designed to carry eight or 10 assault troops, or alternatively freight in the form of an internal or slung payload.

The manufacturer also offers an AS.565 Panther 800 derivative with a powerplant of two 1,322hp (986kW) LHTEC T800-LHT-800 turboshafts and an IBM suite of integrated avionics.

In the United States, the two most important types not already discussed are a pair of Sikorsky helicopters, namely the S-65 twin-engined and S-80 triple-engined variants of the Stallion family, and the Black Hawk land-based and Seahawk shipborne variants of the S-70 family. The larger of these types, by a considerable margin, is the helicopter that has been developed in S-65 and S-80 variants, which resulted from an exacting requirement issued in the early 1960s by the US Marine Corps for an assault helicopter. Sikorsky's work on the S-60 and derived S-64 flying crane helicopter designs stood the company in good stead, for the company responded with its S-65 design that drew on Sikorsky's experience with the S-64 (CH-54 Tarhe) and S-61R (CH-3) in the design of the dynamic system and watertight hull respectively. The US Marine Corps was impressed with the preliminary design, and in August 1962 ordered two YCH-65A prototype and service test helicopters. The first of these machines flew in October 1964 with a powerplant of two 2,850hp (2,125kW) General Electric T64-GE-3 turboshafts, and soon confirmed its ability to lift 38 troops or 24 litters as alternatives to a heavy freight load carried internally or externally.

The S-70B version of Sikorsky's current lightweight military helicopter is used by the US Navy in two forms as the SH-60B Seahawk for the LAMPS III role from smaller warships such as destroyers and cruisers, and as the SH-60F Ocean Hawk for the anti-submarine role from aircraft carriers. If funding permits, it is planned that the SH-60R will be produced as a converted type able to undertake either of these roles by changes in the embarked equipment.

Helicopter Armament

MOST modern military helicopters have provision for armament. Some of these rotary-wing machines are, of course, designed from the beginning for the carriage of specific weapons or types of weapon for the fulfilment of their intended task. Battlefield attack helicopters are generally fitted with a stub wing arrangement carrying four hardpoints for weapons such as multiple launchers for unguided rockets, clusters of air-to-surface missiles optimised for the anti-tank role, machine gun or cannon pods and, increasingly, two or four short-range air-to-air missiles for self-defence; most of these helicopters also carry a trainable cannon, usually between 20mm and 30mm in calibre of 20, for the suppression of ground threats and the engagement of targets of opportunity, the latter including threatening helicopters. Naval helicopters are generally tasked with the anti-submarine and/or anti-ship roles, and for these tasks carry lightweight homing torpedoes (or depth charges) or anti-ship missiles on hardpoints attached to the sides of the fuselage rather than under stub wings. This leaves the utility battlefield helicopter whose tasks are usually the provision of air mobility and the evacuation of the wounded. Such helicopters were initially unarmed, but since the time of the Vietnam War have gradually sprouted the capability for an increasingly wide assortment of weapons ranging from packs of rockets and/or fixed forward-firing cannon or multi-barrel machine guns on the sides of the fuselage under the control of the pilot or co-pilot, via trainable multi-barrel machine gun installations (fed with belted ammunition carried in large magazines installed on the cabin floor) on the sides of the central fuselage and controlled by gunners in a doorway, to trainable multi- or single-barrel machine guns pintle-mounted in a cabin door (or by the rear ramp/door of machines such as the Boeing CH-47 Chinook and Sikorsky CH-53 Sea Stallion/Super Stallion) also under control of gunners. The provision of such armament capability greatly enhances the tactical capabilities of the utility helicopter, for the gunner-operated trainable weapons can protect the helicopter from the attentions of attack helicopters and soften up the ground defences before the embarked troops are landed, and the provision of fixed forward-firing armament contributes to this latter capability as well as opening the possibility of limited close support for the troops after they have disembarked.

The US Marine Corps ordered an eventual 139 examples of the CH-53A initial production model, which entered service in the autumn of 1966. As delivered initially, the CH-53A was fitted with a powerplant of two 2,850hp (2,125kW) T64-GE-6 turboshafts, but later helicopters switched to two 3,080hp (2,297kW) T64-GE-1 turboshafts, and then to two 3,435hp (2,561kW) T64-GE-16 turboshafts for improved performance with a payload that could include one 4.13in (105mm) howitzer and ammunition, or 38 troops, or 24 litters plus four attendants, or more than 8,000lb (3,629kg) of freight carried in the hold, or alternatively more than 13,000lb (5,897kg) of freight carried as a slung load. The hold is 30ft 0in (9.14m) long, 7ft 6in (2.29m) wide and 6ft 6in (1.98m) high, and access is provided by a hydraulically operated ventral ramp/door and a door on the forward starboard side.

All but 32 of the helicopters were built with provision for the towing of a minesweeping sled. Israel operates 30 or more examples of the S-65 family (10 CH-53As supplemented by 20 or more S-65Cs), and is upgrading its fleet in a programme described under the CH-53D. The RH-53A designation was applied to 15 CH-53As transferred to the US Navy, and converted into dedicated minesweepers with a powerplant of two 3,925hp (2,926kW) T64-GE-413 turboshafts and the special winch/quick-release gear required to tow or release minesweeping sleds. The TH-53A designation was allocated to five CH-53As transferred to the USAF as basic qualification trainers.

The HH-53B Super Jolly is the USAF's combat SAR variant, first flown in March 1967 and fitted out with the same provisions as the Sikorsky HH-3E Jolly Green Giant (including a retractable inflight-refuelling probe and all-weather flight instrumentation), and powered by two 3,080hp (2,297kW) T64-GE-3 turboshafts supplied with fuel from an increased internal capacity including auxiliary tanks on external struts cantilevered out from the main fuel-carrying lateral sponsons.

The CH-53C was the pure transport counterpart of the HH-53C for the USAF, which received 20 such helicopters without inflight-refuelling capability, armour, armament or specialised avionics. The helicopters were initially operated for the insertion and extraction of Special Forces, but eight of them were later revised to provide battlefield mobility for the USAF's Mobile Tactical Air Control System. The HH-53C Super Jolly was an important type that was developed as an upgraded version of the HH-53B for the USAF, with greater performance and payload provided by an uprated powerplant comprising two 3,925hp (2,926kW) T64-GE-7 turboshafts for greater performance and payload. Procurement totalled 44 such helicopters with an advanced avionics suite, and these remained operational into the late 1980s.

The CH-53D Sea Stallion is an improved version of the CH-53A for the US Marine Corps, with greater power in the form of two 3,925hp (2,926kW) T64-GE-413 turboshafts for higher performance and increased payload (55 troops or a heavier load of freight) carried over short ranges. Delivery of 126 CH-53Cs was completed in the spring of 1972, and most of these helicopters have provision to tow a minesweeping sled. Two of the helicopters were later converted to VIP transport configuration under the designation VH-53D Sea Stallion. The export variant of the CH-53D is the S-65C, of which Israel operates 22. Israel cannot afford to replace its fleet with the more capable CH-53E model, and therefore in 1990 launched a programme for IAI's MATA subsidiary to upgrade the S-65Cs (together with the 10 CH-53As) to CH-53/2000 (otherwise Yasur 2000) standard. The first revised helicopter flew in June 1992 with structural revisions to the tail, extensive but not full rewiring, new electronic warfare warning systems

Seen here in the form of an MH-53J Super Dragon of the Japanese naval air arm, the Sikorsky S-80M is the dedicated minesweeping version of the S-80E (CH-53E Super Stallion) transport helicopter developed from the S-65 (H-53 Sea Stallion) with a three- rather than two-engined powerplant and large lateral sponsons for a considerably enlarged fuel capacity.

including an improved RWR, and an upgraded avionics suite including a new mission computer, a moving map display, two multi-function displays, an autopilot with added subsystems, and provision for the flightcrew to undertake nap-of-the-earth night flights with the aid of night vision goggles and an HUD.

First flown in October 1972 and built to the extent of 30 helicopters, the RH-53D is the US Navy's dedicated minesweeping version of the CH-53D, with a powerplant of two 4,380hp (3,266kW) T64-GE-415 turboshafts to provide adequate power for the type's exacting role with the AQS-14 minehunting sonar and the towed Mk 103 mechanical, Mk 104 acoustic, Mk 105 magnetic and Mk 106 magnetic/acoustic sweeps, as well as the SPU-1 'Magnetic Orange Pipe' for dealing with shallow-water magnetic mines. The type is also fitted with two 0.5in (12.7mm) Browning M2 heavy machine guns for the detonation of any mines brought to the surface.

The CH-53G is the version of the Sea Stallion series for West Germany, with a powerplant of two T64-GE-7 turboshafts. Sikorsky delivered the first two helicopters in 1969, and Dornier then license-built an additional 110 helicopters.

After evaluating the 'Pave Low II' avionics package for night/adverse-weather navigation and rescue capability in an HH-53B converted to YHH-53H standard, the USAF ordered a 'production' version of this improved HH-53C version as the HH-53H Super Jolly: this type comprises two CH-53Cs and eight HH-53B/Cs converted for the night/adverse-weather SAR role with the 'Pave Low III' sensor suite, which includes the APQ-158 terrain-following/avoidance radar, AAQ-10 IR sensor, provision for two sets of pilot's night vision goggles, and much improved navigational capability (including an INS working in concert with a colour moving-map display and Doppler navigation). In 1986 the helicopters were redesignated MH-53H when modified in the 'Concert Green' programme for the additional capability of inserting and extracting Special Forces teams.

The USAF was not altogether happy with the performance and capabilities of the HH-53H, and the RH-53D had revealed a number of failings when pressed into Special Forces service for the abortive April 1980 attempt to rescue American hostages held in Tehran. The service therefore decided to procure 31 of the improved MH-53J variant (24 HH-53B and

Opposite top: The CH-113 Labrador is the Canadian Armed Forces' search-and-rescue version of the Boeing CH-46A Sea Knight. Some 60 of the type were delivered during 1963-64 to what was then the Royal Canadian Air Force, and in the following year 12 generally similar CH-113A Voyageur helicopters were delivered to the Canadian army.

Opposite bottom: Seen in prototype form, the Bell/Boeing V-22 Osprey is a tilt-rotor aeroplane that has undergone a long development programme troubled by political and economical antipathies more than technical problems. Intended for large-scale service in a number of roles, especially in the assault transport task for the US Marine Corps, the Osprey combines fixed- and rotary-wing attributes, especially in the installation at the wing tips of two powerful turboshafts in nacelles that can be tilted between the vertical and the horizontal. Each of these engines drives a large-diameter 'proprotor' that with their axes vertical work as rotors for vertical take-off and landing, and with their axes horizontal as propellers for propulsion with the weight of the aeroplane supported by the fixed wing.

Right: The Sikorsky UH-60A Black Hawk is a highly versatile utility tactical helicopter for the movements of loads carried internally or externally, and can also be fitted with an external stores-support system for the carriage of additional fuel or weapons.

Below: Another type that has undergone a fairly tortured design and development process leading to a first flight in 1996, the Boeing/Sikorsky RAH-66 Comanche is an advanced helicopter of which much is expected. It was originally planned that production of 5,000 such helicopters would permit the Comanche to replace the Bell UH-1 Iroquois, Bell AH-1 HueyCobra, Bell OH-58 Kiowa and McDonnell Douglas (Hughes) OH-6 Cayuse in a host of light tactical roles, but the procurement total for this advanced 'stealthy' type, which has a structure largely of composite materials, has been steadily eroded to 1,292 machines for use mainly in the scouting role for the McDonnell Douglas AH-64 Apache.

seven HH-53C conversions) for use by the US Special Forces in clandestine and anti-insurgency missions. The converted helicopters were redelivered from July 1987 to a standard that includes a powerplant of two 4,380hp (3,266kW) T64-GE-415 turboshafts, so that performance is not degraded by the increase in maximum take-off weight through use of folding rotors and an additional 1,000lb (454kg) of titanium armour around vital points. Other changes include improvement of the terrain-avoidance/terrain-following radar and IR countermeasures, installation of a missile-warning receiver, retrofit of the original naval folding tail, and addition of new items such as a Texas Instruments AAQ-10 FLIR in a stabilized turret under the inflight-refuelling probe, secure voice communications, and a GPS receiver. The type has provision for two drop tanks and an armament of three 0.3in (7.62mm) Miniguns or three 0.5in (12.7mm) heavy machine guns

In the late 1960s, Sikorsky proposed a derivative of the S-65 (CH-53 Sea Stallion) in which much greater payload could be carried by the replacement of the original two-engined powerplant by a three-engined powerplant driving a larger main rotor. The US Navy was not interested at the time, but the demands of operations during the early 1970s in the Vietnam War persuaded the service to change its attitude, and in 1973 Sikorsky received an order for two YCH-53E prototype and service test helicopters based on its S-80 design. The first of these flew in March 1974, and deliveries of the CH-53E production version for the US Marine Corps began in June 1981. By comparison with the S-65 versions, the S-80 has a third engine (located in the port side of the dorsal fairing aft of the main rotor), a larger main rotor with seven rather than six blades, and a tail rotor of increased diameter. In conjunction with the considerably more powerful dynamic system, the CH-53E's improved payload capability results from its large hold.

The YUH-61A was a prototype of Boeings' (at the time Boeing Vertol) contender in the UTTAS competition won by the Sikorsky YUH-60A that was then placed in production as the UH-60A Black Hawk. The choice between the two helicopter types was difficult, but the Sikorsky machine was finally preferred for its greater versatility, easier partial disassembly for air transport, lower purchase and operating cost, and greater closeness to full production standard.

The US Marine Corps has a requirement for 177 examples of the CH-53E, which are to be upgraded with more powerful 4,750hp (3,542kW) T64-GE-416 turboshafts and fitted with IR suppressors on their exhausts, composite tail rotor blades, Omega navigation, a ground-proximity warning system, an improved internal freight-handling system, a missile warning system,

One of the major limitations of the helicopter had always been its range, resulting primarily from the fact that the engine or engines have to provide all the lifting and propulsive effort required to maintain the helicopter's flight capability. Additional range is an important factor in operations such as combat-search-and-rescue and the infiltration/exfiltration of Special Forces units, and helicopters used for those roles (this is a Sikorsky H-60 Black Hawk) are fitted with a long inflight-refuelling probe. This is installed low on the fuselage and is of the extending type designed to reach forward under the disc swept by the main rotor to make contact with the hose-and-drogue type of refuelling system used by tankers such as this Lockheed KC-130 Hercules, a propeller-driven type with performance that is better matched to that of the helicopter than is possible with any turbojet- or turbofan-powered type such as the Boeing KC-13 Stratotanker.

chaff/flare dispensers, a nitrogen fuel tank inerting system, AIM-9 Sidewinder short-range AAMs for self-defence, and the Northrop Helicopter Night Vision System.

The MH-53E Sea Dragon is the US Navy's mine-countermeasures version of the CH-53E that was developed as the S-80M, and first flew in September 1983 for service from June 1986 against a requirement for 56 such helicopters each able to tow a hydrofoil sled carrying mechanical, acoustic or magnetic sensors. The type has more internal fuel in larger composite-structure sponsons, provision for ferrying fuel in seven tanks carried in the hold, improved electrical and hydraulic systems, and enhanced navigation and automatic flight control systems (the last including capability for automatic towing, and automatic approach to and departure from the hover). In the influence sweeping role, the MH-53E has a maximum useful load of 26,000lb (11,793kg), and its equipment includes the Westinghouse AQS-14 towed sonar as well as options such as the AQS-17 mine neutralisation device, ALQ-141 electronic sweep, and EDO ALQ-166 towed hydrofoil sled (used for the detonation of magnetic mines). The same basic type is available for export as the S-80M, of which Japan has ordered 11.

Designed to meet the US Army's Utility Tactical Transport Aircraft System requirement for a Bell UH-1 Iroquois replacement, able to carry an 11-man infantry squad, the S-70 is of basically conventional configuration with its light alloy fuselage, fixed tailwheel landing gear with a single wheel on each unit, and a dynamic system that includes two turboshafts side-by-side behind the gearbox for the rotor system comprising four-blade main and tail rotors. In many of its features, however, the S-70 offers evidence of advanced aerodynamic, structural and operational thinking. The fuselage, for example, was designed to retain 85 per cent of the cockpit and hold intact after a vertical impact with the ground at 40ft (12.2m) per second; the cockpit provides armour protection for the two pilots; and a sliding door on each side provides access to the hold, which is comparatively large and well planned. The main rotor has blades of advanced aerodynamic design and composite construction (able to withstand cannon hits of up to 23mm calibre without loss of structural integrity) attached to the one-piece forged titanium rotor head by elastomeric (no-lubrication) bearings, and the tail rotor comprises two twin-blade units fastened in a crossbeam arrangement and tilted to port as a means of generating lift as well as anti-torque thrust.

The first of three YUH-60A prototype and service test helicopters flew in October 1974, and in December 1976 the type was declared winner over its Boeing Vertol YUH-61A competitor for selection as the UH-60A production model. The UH-60A entered service in 1979, and is a versatile helicopter able to carry a useful cargo payload (including a 4.13in/105mm howitzer and 50 rounds of ammunition) as an alternative to its standard load of embarked infantrymen. At first there were a number of in-service problems with the transmission, but a new gearbox has been developed to improve reliability and increase maximum take-off weight, which allows the carriage of a greater assortment of external loads as well as improved armament.

The UH-60A is also qualified for the carriage of AGM-114 Hellfire anti-tank missiles and the Honeywell Volcano dispenser system with 950 Gator anti-personnel and anti-vehicle minelets. From 1989 most helicopters have been upgraded in the aircraft survivability equipment (ASE) programme to UH-60A Enhanced Black Hawk standard with Omega navigation, satellite communications, a specific-threat RWR complementing the original general-threat RWR, and provision for the M60 machine gun to be replaced by the M134 Minigun.

The US Army plans a total procurement of 2,262 H-60 series helicopters,

By comparison with the US Army's UH-60 Black Hawk, the US Navy's SH-60 series (Seahawk for the LAMPS III role and Ocean Hawk for the 'CV helo' role from destroyers and aircraft carriers respectively) has a folding main rotor and a folding tail for reduced shipboard hangarage requirement.

and production of the UH-60A reached 985 helicopters before the improved UH-60L was introduced.

The EH-60A is the special electronics mission aircraft (SEMA) variant intended for the interception, monitoring, localisation, and jamming of battlefield communication nets with the 1,800lb (816kg) ALQ-151 'Quick Fix II' ECM system, which is a development of the system originally fitted on the Bell EH-1H Iroquois. The type first flew in YEH-60A prototype form during September 1981, and 66 production helicopters were delivered between 1987 and 1989 with a hover IR suppression subsystem and ASN-32 INS. The helicopters were to have received the revised designation EH-60C Black Hawk after the retrofit of the ASE defensive suite with the APR-39(V)3 RWR and two M130 chaff/flare dispensers as well as the ALQ-156 missile warning system, but the change of designation was not implemented, and the H-60C designation is currently reserved for an EH-60C command and control helicopter that has not yet received any funding.

The core designation H-60B was reserved for the first Seahawk naval version of the S-70 series, and the HH-60D Night Hawk was planned as the USAF's combat SAR variant of the UH-60A, with the dynamic system and rescue winch of the SH-60B. The avionics proposed for this important type included advanced radar, FLIR, Litton INS, and multi-function cockpit and helmet displays. Other equipment included stub wings for two external tanks, a retractable inflight-refuelling probe, and two side-mounted machine guns. The type was cancelled in 1989 after the completion of a single prototype, however, which placed emphasis on the MH-60A Credible Hawk interim version, of which some 30 examples were produced as UH-60A conversions (for the use of the 160th Special Operations Aviation Regiment) with features such as greater fuel capacity, inflight-refuelling capability, FLIR, IR jammer, chaff/flare dispensers, night vision equipment, multi-function cockpit displays, and provision for armament in the form of two door-mounted 0.3in (7.62mm) M134 Miniguns, but neither terrain-following radar nor FLIR. The conversions were effected pending the availability of the MH-60K (replaced by the MH-60L).

There is also an MH-60A Embassy Hawk version optimised for short-notice missions of a classified nature in Europe: this 'contingency mission' variant, of which four have been converted from UH-60A standard, has a number of special features including satellite communications and a GPS receiver. The core designation H-60F was reserved for the second Seahawk naval version of the S-70 series.

The MH-60G Pave Hawk is a considerably improved version of the MH-60A, and was designed for use by the Special Forces as well as combat SAR, and has the same operational features and additional fuel capacity as the MH-60A, plus an inflight-refuelling probe, secure voice communications, satellite communications, electronic map display, weather/mapping radar, Doppler navigation and Litton INS, auxiliary fuel, and various protective items all integrated by a digital databus. Some 103 such helicopters were delivered from 1982 to 1993, but from January 1992 some 82 of them were redesignated as HH-60G Pave Hawk helicopters (to indicate their revision for the combat SAR role), with a rescue hoist, the 'Pave Low III' night/adverse-weather navigation system's Hughes AAQ-16 FLIR, provision for two M134 Minigun door-mounted weapons, and provision for two external units for weapons and/or fuel. The core designations H-60H and H-60J were reserved for the SAR and special warfare versions of the Seahawk naval version of the S-70 series.

The MH-60K Black Hawk was derived from the UH-60L and first flown in August 1990, and is the US Army's special operations aircraft (SOA) version, of which 60 are required for the insertion and extraction of Special Forces' teams under adverse terrain and climatic conditions. The first helicopter was completed in February 1992, and the type has inflight-refuelling capability using an extending probe, weapons capability including provision for FIM-92 Stinger short-range AAMs and pintle mounts strengthened for 0.5in (12.7mm) heavy machine guns, a host of survivability features, a four-screen 'glass' cockpit, and an advanced avionics package. This last is a Boeing responsibility and is based on that of the Boeing Vertol MH-47E Chinook, with features such as Texas Instruments APQ-174A multi-mode terrain-following and terrain-avoidance radar, Hughes AAQ-16 FLIR, night vision equipment and secure communications gear.

First flown in March 1988 for delivery from October 1989, the UH-60L is the UH-60A's successor in the tactical assault transport role. The variant has an uprated transmission and a powerplant of two 1,800hp (1,342kW) T700-GE-701C turboshafts, and this combination restores the performance lost in the UH-60A by addition of 2,000lb (907kg) more payload.

The AH-60L is the direct action penetrator (DAP) conversion of the MH-60L, introduced in 1990 for the use of two platoons of the 160th Special Operations Aviation Regiment. The variant has radar, FLIR and the ESL for forward-firing weapons capability. The MH-60L, a standard to which a few basic transport Black Hawks were modified, is basically similar to the MH-60A, and is to be replaced by the MH-60K. The UH-60M had been proposed as an enhanced version for production from 1992 as a second-generation land-based version with T700-GE-701C turboshafts, the fuselage stretched by 1ft 0in (0.305m), new Sikorsky/Boeing composite-structure main rotor blades of revised section to provide 11 per cent more lift, digital avionics based on a digital databus, an integrated navigation/communications system, a new automatic flight-control system, and a 15 per cent increase in fuel capacity for a 10 per cent increase in range. The type was cancelled during 1989 in favour of the UH-60L.

The VH-60N designation is applied to nine examples of a VIP transport version procured by the US Marine Corps for the movement of the president and high-ranking officials of the US government. The airframe is that of the UH-60A, but the powerplant and some of the avionics are those of the SH-60B, and the rotor is fitted with the brake of the HH-60A. Other modifications include weather radar, additional fuel capacity, hardening against electromagnetic pulse, secure communications, and countermeasures such as exhaust suppression, IR jamming and an optional chaff/flare dispenser.

The UH-60P is the S-70A-18 version of the UH-60L for the South Korean army, with minimal modifications to the avionics. Sikorsky delivered three such helicopters in December 1990, and the remaining 90 are being assembled by Korean Air with an increasing proportion of South Korean components.

The UH-60Q is the casevac version of the UH-60L, of which the US Army

The Sikorsky SH-60B Seahawk is comprehensively equipped not only for the armed role (anti-submarine and anti-ship capabilities with sonobuoys and radar) but also for the detection of incoming threats with its radar and electronic support measures system, the presence of sea-skimming missiles and other such threats being relayed to the parent vessel in real time by a data-link system.

requires 120 conversions that have yet to be funded. The conversion, pioneered in a single prototype, includes an onboard oxygen generation system, patient monitoring equipment, cabin lighting and air-conditioning, personnel location system, rescue hoist, searchlight, FLIR, weather/mapping radar, and enhancements to the navigation, communications and survivability features of the basic helicopter.

The UH-60V is the command and control model with a Symetric Industries improved data modem, for digital communication with armoured fighting vehicles, troops and helicopters, and export helicopters are designated in the S-70A series, which includes the S-70A-12 combat SAR helicopter for Japan, which operates the type as the UH-60J in the hands of the Japanese Air Self-Defense Force (46) and Japanese Maritime Self-Defense force (18). Procurement started with one imported helicopter and two helicopters assembled from American-supplied kits (first flown in February 1990), and is now all-Japanese.

The naval version of the S-70 series is known to the manufacturer as the S-70B and to the US Navy as the Seahawk or, for more specialised roles, by other hawk names. This maritime S-70B version was produced to meet the US Navy's light airborne multi-purpose system (LAMPS) Mk III requirement for a helicopter to replace the Sikorsky SH-3 Sea King on destroyers and larger frigates, and to complement the lighter Kaman SH-2F Seasprite LAMPS Mk I helicopter on smaller surface vessels. Although the S-70B was derived from the land-based S-70A (UH-60 Black Hawk), extensive changes had to be effected in the airframe and systems to allow the incorporation of the shipborne variant's anti-submarine and anti-ship missile defence equipment, but the most obvious external difference

Opposite: One of the great tactical advantages of the helicopter is its ability to collect and/or deliver a slung load out of and/or into an area inaccessible to a fixed-wing aeroplane. This greatly enhances the overall capabilities of the helicopter for battlefield tasks such as the repositioning of equipment (such as this light assault gun carried by a Sikorsky CH-53E Super Stallion), and the delivery of supplies such as fuel and ammunition.

Below: With a triple-engined powerplant driving a seven-blade main rotor, heavily laden helicopters such as these Sikorsky S-80 (H-53E Super Stallion and Sea Dragon series) machines have a prodigious thirst for fuel that can be satisfied long-endurance or long-range missions only by use of drop tanks and/or inflight-refuelling from aircraft such as the Lockheed KC-130 Hercules.

between the UH-60 and SH-60 is the latter's modified landing gear, with its tail unit revised to twin-wheel layout and moved forward several feet to provide the shorter wheel base required for safe flight operations from the relatively modest flight platforms of the US Navy's smaller warships. Other changes include a folding main rotor with a rotor brake, a recovery assist and secure traverse (RAST) downhaul system providing the capability of landing on small naval vessels under adverse weather and sea conditions, a rescue hoist, and buoyancy devices.

The S-70B design was declared winner of the LAMPS Mk III competition in 1977, and the first of five YSH-60B prototype and service test helicopters flew in December 1979, paving the way for the first of a planned 260 SH-60B production helicopters to enter service in 1983: in 1994 procurement was ended after the delivery of 188 helicopters.

The SH-60F Ocean Hawk is the four-man SH-60B version designed to replace the Sikorsky SH-3 Sea King as the inner-zone anti-submarine helicopter carried by aircraft carriers. The concept was evaluated through a converted SH-60B that first flew in March 1987, and production helicopters entered service from March 1990: procurement was halted prematurely in 1994 after the delivery of 82 helicopters against a requirement for 150 such machines. The 'CV Helo' configuration differs from that of the SH-60B in its lack of LAMPS Mk III equipment (including the RAST downhaul system, cargo hook and radar for the detection of anti-ship missiles), but its construction with a digital databus allows the installation of a different avionics suite including the ASQ-13F dunking sonar, ASQ-81 MAD with a towed 'bird', ALQ-142 ESM system, and ARQ-44 data link to provide the data for the generation of a fire-control solution for a weapon fit that includes up to three lightweight anti-submarine torpedoes, two of them on the extended port hardpoint; these torpedoes can be either the obsolescent Mk 46 or advanced Mk 50 Barracuda.

The SH-60F can carry only eight sonobuoys compared with the SH-60B's figure of 25, but the ambient underwater noise levels of its inner-zone tasking make the dunking sonar altogether more important as the type's primary acoustic sensor. The sonar data are fed to the twin ASN-150 tactical navigation systems that drive two large multi-function displays (one on the instrument panel and the other at the sensor operator's station) and four central display units. Other elements of the tactical navigation system are the TACAN and Doppler Tactical Navigation systems, of which the latter has provision for GPS update.

The SH-60F is powered by two 1,900hp (1,417kW) T700-GE-401C turboshafts for a sustained high level of performance despite its higher maximum take-off weight.

Entering service from January 1990 after a first flight in August 1988, the HH-60H Rescue Hawk is the US Navy's helicopter combat support (combat SAR) and Special Forces variant of the SH-60B Seahawk, with the SH-60F Ocean Hawk's powerplant of two T700-GE-401C turboshafts. The US Navy plans a total of 18 helicopters of this type, which has the tasks of recovering a four-man crew at a radius of 288 miles (463km) and delivering an eight-man commando team to a point 3,000ft (915m) above their destination at a radius of 230 miles (370km). The variant's avionics include the APR-39A(XE)2 RWR, AVR-2 laser warning receiver and AAR-47 missile-approach warning system to trigger two ALE-39 chaff/flare launchers and/or one

Above: The Kamov Ka-32 'Helix' is the civil variant of the military helicopter in Russian service as the Ka-27, Ka-28, Ka-29 and Ka-31 series. The type is clearly a lineal successor to the Ka-25 series in its basic design with superimposed co-axial main rotors, but has more advanced systems, a larger cabin, and an uprated powerplant.

Right: The European Helicopter Industries EH.101 is a collaborative British and Italian type that was initially ordered in its shipborne version but which has since been contracted in its land-based utility military variant.

ALQ-144 'hot brick' IR jammer. The type's armament includes two 0.3in (7.62mm) M60D machine guns pintle-mounted in the cabin doors, but in October 1991 it was decided that the type should be qualified to carry, on its optional hardpoints, additional weapons such as the AGM-114 Hellfire ASM, multiple launcher for 2.75in (70mm) unguided rockets, and gun/cannon pods. The type has a crew of four (night vision goggles and associated equipment being carried for the two pilots) and can carry a commando team of up to 10 men.

First flown in August 1989 for a service debut in 1990 as partial replacement for the Sikorsky HH-3F Pelican, the HH-60J Jayhawk is the US Coast Guard's medium-range SAR helicopter, and as a counterpart to the HH-60H is also derived from the SH-60B. The type has a crew of four and has a radius of at least 345 miles (555km), with a loiter capability of 45 minutes at extreme range, where at least six persons can be recovered from the surface.

SH-60R is the standard to which surviving SH-60B Seahawk and SH-60F Ocean Hawk helicopters are to be rebuilt, assuming the availability of adequate financing, with provision for fully interchangeable equipment so that the helicopters can operate in the SH-60B or SH-60F roles as the tactical situation demands. Export helicopters of the Seahawk type are designated in the S-70B core system, and include the S-70B-3 for Japan, where it is known as the SH-60J.

The Soviets (now the Russians) did not need to emulate the assault transport capability provided to the US Marine Corps by the S-65 and S-80 series of Sea Stallion and Super Stallion helicopters for the amphibious role, but felt the need for a heavy transport type that could be built in utility form for civil and military use. The result is the Mil Mi-26 'Halo'. First flown in December 1977, the Mi-26 is the world's largest production helicopter, and is a highly capable heavy-lift machine scaled up from the Mi-6 but with proportionally more power, in the form of two 9,992hp (7,450kW) ZMDB 'Progress' (Lotarev) D-136 turboshafts, to drive an eight-blade main rotor. As with other such Soviet helicopters, the large hold is accessed by clamshell rear doors and a ramp for the loading of vehicles and pieces of

artillery. The hold is 39ft 4.25in (12.00m) long (increased to 49ft 2.5in (15.00m) if the ramp is kept open), the width is 10ft 6in (3.20m) and the height varies between 9ft 8in (2.95m) and 10ft 4.75in (3.17m). Up to 85 troops or 44,092lb (20,000kg) of freight can be carried in the hold, or alternatively the same amount of freight can be lifted as a slung load.

The Mi-26A is a development of the baseline Mi-26 with a PNK-90 integrated flight and navigation system; the Mi-26MS is the medevac/casevac version of the baseline Mi-26 with a life-support section for four litters and two medical personnel, a surgical section for one litter and three medical personnel, a pre-operation section with accommodation for two litters and two medical personnel, an ambulance section with accommodation for five litters, three seated casualties and two medical personnel, a laboratory section, and a utilities section with lavatory, washing facilities and galley; the Mi-26TM is the flying crane version of the baseline Mi-26 with an undernose gondola for the pilot and sling operator, and a rear gondola for a pilot and trainee; and the Mi-26TZ is the tanker version of the baseline Mi-26 with provision for the carriage of 3,088.4Imp gal (14,040 litres) of fuel, and 228.75Imp gal (1,040 litres) of lubricants that can be dispensed to waiting vehicles via four hoses.

The Mi-26M is an uprated version currently under development with a powerplant of two D-127 turboshafts, each rated at about 14,016hp (10,450kW) for improved hot-and-high capability with the same maximum payload as the baseline Mi-26, or with an increased 55,115lb (25,000kg) payload under standard operating conditions.

Such is the cost of helicopter development and procurement today that considerable efforts have been made to boost collaborative projects such as that for the Eurocopter Tigre/Tiger. The two most important of these, although neither type has yet entered service, are the European Helicopter Industries EH.101, involving Agusta of Italy and Westland of the UK for the creation of a utility helicopter with naval, military and civil applications; and the NH Industries NH-90, involving Agusta, Eurocopter Deutschland, Eurocopter France, and Fokker of the Netherlands for the creation of a utility helicopter with naval and military applications.

The naval model of the European Helicopter Industries EH.101 is called Merlin by the Royal Navy, which is currently the largest customer for the type.

Glossary

AERODYNAMIC LIFT type of lift created by the movement of an aerofoil-shaped body through the air (or vice versa), the more highly curved upper surface producing a low-pressure area that the higher-pressure air under the surface tries to fill, thereby generating lift

ANTI-TORQUE ROTOR small vertically mounted rotor located at the tail to counterbalance the torque reaction of the main rotor

ARTICULATED ROTOR rotor system in which there are flapping hinges, drag hinges and pitch-change bearings between the rotor head and the root of each blade

AUTOGIRO type of rotary-wing aeroplane perfected by de la Cierva with an unpowered main rotor

AUTOGYRO Autogiro-type rotary-wing aeroplane designed by anyone other than de la Cierva and his licensees

CO-AXIAL ROTORS two rotors turning on a common axis with one shaft rotating inside the other

COLLECTIVE PITCH CONTROL system to control the rise or descend of a helicopter by the simultaneous (collective) increase or decrease of the pitch angle of all the main rotor blades

CONTRA-ROTATING ROTORS two rotors turning on a common axis in opposite directions with one shaft rotating inside the other

COUNTER-ROTATING ROTORS two rotors turning on separate axes in opposite directions

CYCLIC PITCH CONTROL system to control the direction of a helicopter in level flight by consecutive (cyclic) altering of the pitch angle of each main rotor blade according to its geometric position during each revolution, thereby tilting the theoretical axis of rotation in the direction of flight desired

DRAG HINGE also known as a lag hinge, this is a hinge in the main rotor's vertical plane near the root of each blade permitting each blade to move freely backward and forward in the horizontal plane independently of the other blades and the rotor hub to eliminate bending moments

FLAP HINGE hinge in the main rotor's horizontal plane near the root of each blade permitting each blade to flap (rise or fall) in the vertical plane independently of the other blades

RIGID ROTOR type of main rotor lacking blade articulation or flexibility: the blades can therefore change pitch and the whole rotor disc can see-saw on the rotor shaft, but the individual blades are not fitted with drag or flap hinges

ROTOR HEAD unit connecting the rotor shaft and main rotor with provision for collective and cyclic pitch control mechanisms

SEMI-RIGID ROTOR type of main rotor without provision for blade articulation (no drag or flap hinges) but offering limited flexibility in the drag and flap planes and also free to see-saw about the rotor shaft

TORQUE REACTION tendency of the motor (and anything attached to it) to turn in the opposite direction to the rotor driven by this motor

Index